JACK R. LEIGHTON, Ph.D., University of Oregon, is Head of the Division of Health, Physical Education, Recreation and Athletics, Chairman of the Department of Men's Physical Education, and Professor of Physical Education, at Eastern Washington State College, and has taught also at Pennsylvania State University. During World War II he served in the United States Army as an administrator of physical reconditioning programs at the service-command and hospital-center levels, and was subsequently Executive Assistant in the Physical Medicine Rehabilitation Service at the Veterans Administration Hospital, Vancouver, Washington. Dr. Leighton has written for such journals as *The Research Quarterly*, *Archives of Physical Medicine and Rehabilitation*, and the *Journal of the AAHPER*.

PROGRESSIVE
WEIGHT TRAINING

Jack R. Leighton

EASTERN WASHINGTON STATE COLLEGE

THE RONALD PRESS COMPANY • NEW YORK

Library of Congress Catalog Card Number: 61-7742
PRINTED IN THE UNITED STATES OF AMERICA

To the late
Ralph Waldo Leighton, Ph.D., D.Sc.,
Dean Emeritus of the School of Health
and Physical Education, University of
Oregon, my father and the person responsible for my interest in weight
training.

Preface

This book is for all who are interested in body development and conditioning through weight training or progressive resistance exercises. In recent years training with weights has spread widely: in individual body building at home or at health studios, in the physical rehabilitation of the hospitalized, in the physical education programs of schools and colleges, and in the conditioning of athletes. Not only does this book provide full exercise sequences for boys, but it also presents a separate and complete program specifically designed for girls. And although the illustrations picture boys and girls demonstrating them, the exercises in this book are equally suitable for adolescents and adults.

A basic program is presented for boys and men who wish to develop body strength and flexibility through an effective method of conditioning. This program, using principally a barbell and fairly heavy weights, consists of 15 fundamental exercises that are designed to develop symmetrically all the major muscle groups and with repeat emphasis on arm and leg muscles.

Increasingly girls and women are exercising with weights in order to improve their general body condition, lose or gain weight, reapportion measurements, firm up slack muscles, and strengthen weak areas. Likewise for them this book provides a series of 17 fundamental exercises mainly for hips, thighs, bust and waist, although all major muscle groups are included. These exercises use only light dumbbells and metal shoes for the most part.

In addition to these two basic programs, special sequences of exercises for systematically developing the various body areas are set forth. Using the exercises of the basic programs, these special sequences also supply 50 further exercises with full explanations of how to do them. Those exercises that are suitable for girls and women are indicated by an asterisk.

Description and explanation of each exercise is given in terms of the starting position and the movements of the exercise (both being also pictured in an accompanying illustration), recommended resistance and starting repetitions, cadence, pointers and cautions to observe, and the principal muscle areas benefited.

For the physical education instructor the book provides materials on presenting progressive weight training in the educational program, methods of conducting classes and of evaluating improvement, basic equipment lists, recommended exercises for developing physical skills and for helping correct postural deviations and weak joints. The athletic coach will be interested, of course, in the conditioning aspects as well as in the special exercises for improving basic physical skills. And the studio operator will find value in both the basic and the advanced programs as they may be used to meet the needs of health studio clientele. For those interested in competitive weight lifting the book closes with an introduction to the sport and instructions for performing the Olympic lifts.

The author would like to express his appreciation to Jack Benson, Joe Barrow, and Ed Spetch, Jr., for posing for the boys' exercise and measurement illustrations; to Orva Gemmell, Beverly Haney, and Joy Lowe for posing for the girls' exercise and measurement illustrations; to Dr. Harold Stevens and Robert Felker for posing for their respective photographs; to John Terpak of York, Pennsylvania, for the information on weight lifting and physique contest scoring; to Mrs. Sharon Boutz for typing the manuscript; and to my wife Helen for so patiently going over portions of the manuscript.

Jack R. Leighton

Cheney, Washington
September, 1960

Contents

PROGRESSIVE WEIGHT TRAINING

1

Introduction

In noting the title of this book, *Progressive Weight Training,* the reader might well raise the questions: Why the term weight training? Doesn't the person lift weights? Then, why not call it weight lifting? The semantics of the terms are not too important in themselves; but the activity is one that has grown to popularity through much misunderstanding, misconception, and prejudice, which makes it rather important that one specifies exactly what particular phase of the activity he is discussing.

A DEFINITION OF TERMS

Three phases of this activity will be defined here to help clarify the situation for the reader as he proceeds through the book. The first two of these are actually phases of the activity; the third is one that can develop, and often does, with a person who engages in this activity with no previous knowledge or instruction concerning it.

WEIGHT LIFTING. This term refers to the sport phase of the activity where actual competition between individuals and teams takes place. In this phase, there are weight divisions for competition just as there are in boxing and wrestling. Competition is between individuals within a specific weight division. The weight divisions are: 123¼ lbs., 132¼ lbs., 148¾ lbs., 165¼ lbs., 181¼ lbs., 198¼ lbs., and heavyweight. The contestants within each weight division compete with one another as to the total amount of weight lifted as a composite of three recognized two-arm lifts: the press, the snatch, and the clean and jerk. (The method of performing each of these lifts is explained in Chapter 7.) In case of a tie within a weight division, the victory goes to the man lightest in bodyweight. Team winners are determined much in the same manner as are team winners in a track meet—by points won for placing within the various weight divisions.

WEIGHT TRAINING. This term refers to the exercise phase of the activity where weight, in the form of barbells and dumbbells, is used to condition and alter the size of various segments of the body. This is, undoubtedly, the most popular phase. Here the underdeveloped individual strives for average or above-average size in terms of muscular bulk and bodyweight; the overweight person strives for reduced bodyweight and size; the athlete

3

strives for increased strength and condition to become a better performer in his chosen sport; and those who desire perfection in bodily development may strive for this and achieve their reward by becoming a place winner in one of the many physique contests sponsored through the A.A.U. Weight training is enjoyed as much by women as by men. It is with this phase of the activity, and the method of conducting it in the school or club program, that this book will be primarily concerned.

WEIGHT STRAINING. Actually not a phase of the activity, it is what often happens when someone unfamiliar with the field first comes in contact with a set of weights. His first step is usually to find out how much weight he can lift either in a competitive lift or in an exercise. The result in such a case can be harmful, particularly if the individual is not in good physical condition. The writer well remembers lifting a heavy barbell from the shoulders of a novice who entered the weight room unnoticed, proceeded to the squat rack which is shoulder high, lifted the bar onto his shoulders, and made a one-way trip to the floor in the squat or deep-knee-bend exercise. This does not mean that the use of weights should in any way be considered harmful. It does mean, however, that the weights should be respected. There is a proper and an improper method of performing each lift and exercise. There is a reason for this proper method. It should be learned and mastered.

BACKGROUND OF WEIGHT LIFTING

To say with accuracy just when man first engaged in weight lifting as a competitive activity or a means of exercise is, of course, impossible. Prehistoric men may have engaged in contests with one another to determine who could lift the heaviest stones. Jowett, in his book *The Key to Might and Muscle,* presents an illustration of barbells used in training Chinese youths—a custom, he states, that dates back to the time of Confucius.[1]

Greek mythology credits the beginning of progressive weight resistance exercise to a man named Milo who lived in Crotona, Greece. According to the story, Milo wanted to become the strongest man, not merely in all of Greece, but in the entire world. To accomplish this mission, he began to lift a young bull when he was a small lad. As the bull increased in size, so Milo increased in strength; and when the bull was fully-grown, Milo had developed sufficient strength, not only to lift this fully-grown animal, but also to carry it around on his shoulders.

According to one version of the story,[2] Milo entered the Olympic stadium carrying the bull upon his shoulders, as trumpets blared, and pro-

[1] George F. Jowett, *The Key to Might and Muscle* (Philadelphia: Milo Publishing Co., 1926); illustrations between pp. 112 and 113.

[2] Harry Rosen, "Milo of Crotona—Did He Originate Progressive Exercise?" *Strength and Health,* Vol. 4, No. 10 (September 1936), pp. 8, 9, and 37.

ceeded twice around the arena. After setting the animal down, he engaged in wrestling competition and won the Olympic championship—a title he held for twenty-five years.

Fig. 1—1. Karl Swaboda.

Courtesy of Ray Van Cleef

Weight lifting and weight training did not gain acceptance to any extent until the beginning of the twentieth century. Before our time barbells and dumbbells were thick-handled, large, and cumbersome. The equipment was suited for use only in gymnasiums and by ponderous men with large hands. The lifts performed were of a slower type and involved more brute strength and little of the skill required in modern-day lifting. Very few engaged in the activity for any purpose.

One of the old-time Europeans of this ponderous type was Karl Swoboda of Vienna, Austria; he is credited with a continental jerk (a two-handed overhead lift) of 423 lbs. As was typical of many of these men, his great strength was matched by an equally great appetite. One story [3] records his dissatisfaction with the size of a steak, approximately six inches by five inches, that was served him in a restaurant when he was visiting a friend in Paris. His friend, not wishing to displease him, told him that it was but a sample to determine if the steak would be satisfactory. Swoboda was pleased. He ate the steak, found it to his satisfaction, and then proceeded to eat six more just like the first.

AMERICAN BACKGROUND. America had some of these ponderous lifters before the turn of the century, such as Canada's Louis Cyr who is credited

[3] Gord Venables, "Swoboda and The Seven Steaks," *Strength and Health,* Vol. 6, No. 6 (May 1938), pp. 16, 17, and 50.

with a back lift of 4,300 lbs., and was described in the 1920's as the strongest man who ever lived.[4] Men such as these, however, were not responsible for the greater popularity of weight lifting at the turn of the century. On

Courtesy of Ray Van Cleef

Fig. 1—2. Eugene Sandow.

the contrary, largely responible for the idea that has accompanied this activity down to the present day: that those who engaged in weight lifting were large and slow men. This was true in that ponderous men found success in the activity. It does not mean, however, that engaging in weight lifting caused them to be large and slow, although this is often erroneously implied by the statement.

In the 1890's, a strong man known professionally as Eugene Sandow was giving weight-lifting and physique-posing demonstrations in Philadelphia and other cities in the East. Strong, equally handsome, and possessing a fine physique, Sandow was small when compared with the other strong men of that and earlier times. His demonstrations were seen by many, but probably few were more impressed than one Alan Calvert. Sandow became Calvert's ideal for masculine shape and development.

Calvert felt that there were many men the country over who would like to develop a similar physique if they but had the means. To provide the means he founded the Milo Bar Bell Company in April 1902 and sold adjustable barbells and exercise courses by mail. His equipment was smaller than the heavier solid weights of the past, and the adjustable feature greatly enhanced its capabilities. Calvert published his first substantial book *The*

[4] George Jowett, *The Strongest Man That Ever Lived* (Philadelphia: Milo Publishing Co., 1927).

Truth About Weight Lifting in 1911, and his most complete treatise, *Super Strength,* in 1924. In 1914 he began the publication of a magazine entitled *Strength* that dealt with various aspects of weight training and weight lifting. George F. Jowett took over this barbell and publishing company from 1924 to 1926, and Mark H. Berry from 1926 until its demise in 1935. Several books on the subject of weight training and weight lifting were published during these times by both Jowett and Berry.

In 1932 the York Barbell Company was founded by Robert C. Hoffman and a new magazine, *Strength and Health,* appeared on the newstands. This barbell company and its publications are probably the best known of any now being marketed. Hoffman knew the art of selling much better than did his predecessors, and he is probably the one individual most responsible for the rise in popularity of weight training and lifting in the United States.

During World War II weight training gained considerable attention, particularly in the physical reconditioning and rehabilitation programs of the armed forces. Here the equipment was used in bringing the atrophied muscles of disabled service men back to normal and in maintaining muscle tonus in the unaffected muscles of the hospitalized. This popularity has carried over into the rehabilitation programs of the Veterans Administration, communities, and private organizations.

Following World War II, many health studios have been established, particularly in the larger cities of the nation. These studios specialize in fancy exercise equipment and cleanliness of establishment, and they have programs for both men and women. Most of these studios are operated by persons whose special training has been the success they have achieved in the development of their own bodies.

The reader will have noticed that the history of this activity has been one of growth outside of the physical education profession and outside of our school programs. In the late 1930's and early 1940's few colleges and practically no secondary schools offered weight training as one of the activities in their physical education programs. Since World War II, however, it has become more accepted as a valuable activity in the physical education program. Many colleges now offer such courses for men, and a number of high schools have followed suit. Weight training programs for women have gained acceptance in only a few schools at present but their popularity is sure to grow.

INFLUENCE OF THE WOMEN.   Women, too, have their place in the history of weight lifting and progressive weight training, even though it has not been as prominent as that of the men. Katie Sandwina, a professional strong woman, has been credited with a clean and jerk lift (two hands overhead) of 286 lbs. Lillian Leitzel, a small, feminine woman who weighed less than 100 lbs. performed Roman Ring work with a circus during the 1920's. It is interesting to note that she is credited with 27 right-hand and 17 left-hand chins. This feat takes on even more significance when compared to the one-hand chin record for men which is reported as being approximately 12. Both ladies were sufficiently feminine to attract husbands.

Most of the magazines associated with weight training that have appeared on the newstands have had special sections for women. Margaret Sargent and Marjorie Heathcote wrote for *Strength* magazine; Emily Gay and Phyllis Jowett wrote for *The Body Builder*. Probably the best known are Abbye "Pudgy" Stockton and Vera Christensen, the former and the present women's editor of *Strength and Health* magazine.

In our culture, strength has been associated with men and softness and femininity with women. Most women do not desire to develop strength because in doing so they are afraid they will acquire large muscles and become less feminine. This is a groundless fear. Actually muscles help to give shape to the body. If shape is present without muscular development, then this is either an angular shape given by the bones or a more lumpy shape produced by the presence of body fat. A certain amount of muscular development is a necessity for all persons. Women will actually be more attractive because of it than without it. Fat areas will be reduced and flabby or loose areas will become firm through proper diet and exercises to bring about this necessary muscular development. At Eastern Washington College of Education, the girls in the weight-training program lost, on the average, one inch in circumference from each of three areas—the thigh, the hips, and the waist—and some added to their bust measurements. They felt better physically at the completion of the course than they did at its beginning. The qualities of physical fitness are every bit as desirable in a woman as they are in a man. Possessing them will not make a woman less feminine and certainly not less attractive. After all, many beauty contest winners and professional models use this method to maintain their attractiveness.

FANTASIES AND FACTS ABOUT WEIGHT TRAINING

Some of the major reasons for weight training and weight lifting developing outside of the school program as they did were the claims that harmful effects would result from participating in the activity. The individual's muscles would become enlarged. He would become slow. He would become awkward. He would become "muscle-bound." Few activities ever had as many obstacles to overcome before gaining acceptance. In a way, this was unfortunate, but in another way it was good in that a number of research studies have been conducted to check the claims. Of all the claims, probably the most common and the most investigated is that of becoming "muscle-bound."

Just where the term "muscle-bound" originated is not known, but it was used as early as 1879 by Blaikie although not in reference to weight lifters.[5] He was deriding the condition of the sturdy laborer who, he claimed, was unable to slap the palms of his hands together behind his shoulders. Berry in 1930 claimed that there was "no such thing as muscle-bound." [6] He stated that the average beginner in weight-training exercises had no endurance or suppleness to speak of and that it is only sound logic that one cannot remove something that does not exist. He also wrote: "The champions in no line of sport are expected to excel in other specialties. It is all a matter of mastering one thing and excelling in that one specialty, but we feel safe in making the statement that the average weight lifter is a better all-round performer and has a higher average combination of speed, suppleness and endurance than the average specialist in any other line of sport." Present-day evidence bears out his claim, particularly in regard to the value of weight training as a means of improving performance in other sports. Berry believed that the derogatory statements concerning weight training originated with "light exercise, calisthenic drill" proponents and instructors who were attempting to degrade the activity of weight training in order to build up clientele in their own specialties. The accuracy of such a claim would be difficult to substantiate, particularly since there is evidence of the use of the term "muscle-bound" prior to the establishment of the first train-you-by-mail barbell company in this country in 1902.

Regardless of origin, derogatory claims concerning the effects of weight training upon the body did, and still do, exist. Some of the first studies of the effects of weight training came from the medical field where doctors had been introduced to the activity in rehabilitation programs during World War II. Several such studies dealing with the restoration of muscle power by weight-resistance exercises were performed by DeLorme with the findings being reported in several medical publications.[7] Research workers in physical education have also worked in this field and have produced results which are of interest.[8]

Let us look at this term "muscle-bound" rather closely. The dictionary defines it as: "Having some of the muscles tense and enlarged and of im-

[5] William Blaikie, *How To Get Strong and How To Stay So* (New York: Harper and Bros., 1879), p. 18.

[6] Mark H. Berry, *Physical Training Simplified* (Philadelphia: Milo Publishing Co., 1930), pp. 20-27.

[7] T. L. DeLorme, "Restoration of Muscle Power by Heavy Resistance Exercises," *Journal of Bone and Joint Surgery*, Vol. 27 (October 1945), p. 645.

T. L. DeLorme, "Heavy Resistance Exercises," *Archives of Physical Medicine*, Vol. 27 (October 1946), p. 607.

[8] Edward K. Capen, "The Effect of Systematic Weight Training on Power, Strength, and Endurance," *Research Quarterly*, Vol. 21, No. 2 (May 1950), pp. 83-93.

Edward Chui, "The Effect of Systematic Weight Training on Athletic Power," *Research Quarterly*, Vol. 21, No. 3 (October 1950), pp. 188-94.

John W. Masley, Ara Hairabedian, and Donald Donaldson, "Weight Training in Relation to Strength, Speed and Coordination," *Research Quarterly*, Vol. 24, No. 3 (October 1953), pp. 308-15.

paired elasticity—a condition sometimes produced by excessive athletic exercise." [9]

Now, there is no question about the muscles of an individual becoming enlarged, or hypertrophied, when one engages in a weight-training program specifically designed for this purpose. This is a physiological fact. The degree of enlargement, however, is based upon several factors: first of all, heredity. Each person differs from the next in terms of his potentialities. All men will not be able to develop a 17-inch "bicep" or upper arm. A large man with heavy bones and considerable muscular bulk would probably have very little difficulty in achieving this goal, whereas a shorter, lighter-boned man would probably never be able to attain it. His attainment, however, would undoubtedly be far beyond his present measurement and equally impressive in terms of his size.

The second factor is more directly related to the activity. The degree of enlargement will be somewhat dependent upon the manner in which the person approaches the activity; i.e., his purpose in working with weights. A man striving for physical perfection so that he may win an award in a physique contest will certainly go about his workouts in a different manner than will a young lady who is attempting to trim down her figure. Both, however, will be training with weights. In the latter case the circumference of the young lady's arm may actually become considerably smaller although the muscle becomes stronger, since she will not use sufficient resistance to appreciably affect muscular bulk even though she will be developing a fair degree of strength and will, at the same time, be removing the loose, flabby material (fat) that surrounds and impregnates the muscle.

Now, if the muscles become greatly enlarged through weight training to such an extent that the person may win the title of "Mr. Universe" or, with the accompanying increase in strength, may be able to establish a world's record in weight lifting, the next question is: "Will this muscular bulk be tight, causing a resultant loss of elasticity?" If this is true, the individual would be restricted in the amount of movement possible at the various joints (elbow, shoulder, hip, etc.) of the body and have, as the dictionary states, muscles that are tense and of impaired elasticity. This, however, is not the case. In fact, the opposite is more nearly accurate; i.e., after engaging in a program of progressive weight training, the individual will find movement at these joints less restricted than before.

The writer [10] found significantly greater movement in 27 of 30 joint movements measured following an 8-week period of weight training than at the beginning of the exercise period. (The exercise program followed was that described for boys and men in Chapter 3 of this book.) In another

[9] *Webster's New Collegiate Dictionary*, 6th ed. (Springfield: G. and C. Merriam Co., 1956), p. 555.
[10] Jack R. Leighton, "Are Weight Lifters Muscle Bound?" *Strength and Health* (March 1956), pp. 16, 44-46.

study [11] the writer found that the national champion weight lifters and winners of the "Mr. America" and "Mr. Universe" titles (indicating they possess the best-developed muscular physiques) exceeded (possessed greater range of movement) the flexibility of the average 16-year-old boy in 15 of 30 joints measured, were exceeded by him in only 5 movements, and equalled him in the remaining 10. To further illustrate this point, the writer would call the reader's attention to the Kraus-Weber tests of physical fitness used in a comparison study of European youth and American youth.[12] One of the tests in this battery was the floor-touch test which 8 per cent of the European youth and 44 per cent of the American youth failed. This movement involves, primarily, hip flexion and extension (a forward and backward movement at the hip joint). In the study referred to above, the average range of movement at this joint for American 16-year-old boys was 55 degrees while the average for champion weight lifters and body builders was 97 degrees. The evidence indicates that even the champion weight lifters and body builders who possess the ultimate in body strength and muscular bulk are more flexible than the average boy of sixteen years in a majority of the movements of the body. Truly then, this tenseness and impaired elasticity, as implied by the term "muscle-bound," are not the result of weight training or lifting or of enlarged muscular size. These and other studies [13] indicate that flexibility or the range of movement at the various joints (provided these joints are normal) is dependent upon the movement patterns to which the joint has become accustomed, and the range of joint movement required for the performance of most weight training exercises usually exceeds the accustomed range for most individuals; hence, the increase in the range of movement recorded at so many of the joints. To increase the range of movement at a joint, one needs to increase the movement pattern. To decrease the range of joint movement, one needs to decrease the movement pattern. The exercises in this book stress this principle.

As to the other harmful effects attributed to weight training, we find much the same story. "He would become slow." A study by Zorbas and Karpovich tells us an opposite story.[14] In this study on the speed of muscular contractions, weight lifters were found to have the fastest reactions of three groups measured. A group of physical education major students was second, and a group of college students engaging in fewer physical activities

11 Jack R. Leighton, "Flexibility Characteristics of Three Specialized Skill Groups of Champion Athletes," *Archives of Physical Medicine and Rehabilitation*, Vol. 38, No. 9 (September 1957), pp. 580-83.

12 Robert H. Boyle, "The Report That Shocked The President," *Sports Illustrated*, Vol. 3, No. 7 (August 15, 1955), pp. 30-33 and 72-73.

13 Jack R. Leighton, "Flexibility Characteristics of Four Specialized Skill Groups of College Athletes," *Archives of Physical Medicine and Rehabilitation*, Vol. 38, No. 1 (January 1957), pp. 24-28.

14 William S. Zorbas and Peter V. Karpovich, "The Effect of Weight Lifting Upon the Speed of Muscular Contractions," *Research Quarterly*, Vol. 22, No. 2 (May 1951), pp. 145-148.

was the slowest. "He would become awkward." A study by Calvin [15] and one by the writer [16] indicate a different story here also. Calvin reported that there was no indication that muscular development associated with weight training over a four-month period of time had in any way a deleterious effect on the motor coordination of a group of high school boys. In fact, the results seemed to indicate that progressive weight-training exercises tend to affect favorably their motor coordination. The writer found a signficant increase in the agility of college men following a ten-week period of weight-training exercises.

The evidence, therefore, opposes the claims of harmful effects and favors weight training as an activity that produces desirable physical results. There may be such a condition as "muscle-bound," but engaging in a properly directed program of progressive weight training does not result in this condition. Other physical benefits of participation in such a program are: increased strength, endurance, balance, and power, all of which contribute to better physical fitness, health, and athletic achievement.

PURPOSES AND BENEFITS OF PROGRESSIVE WEIGHT TRAINING

Many of the benefits that may be derived from progressive weight training have been listed above. However, in terms of the activity as a unit of work in an over-all physical education program, the objectives in terms of students' needs might read as follows:

BOYS' OR MEN'S PROGRAM

1. To develop in the individual bodily strength and flexibility primarily, and also to develop agility, speed, and endurance
2. To teach the proper method of lifting weights
3. To familiarize the student with an effective method of body conditioning and development that may be carried on in after-school years
4. To give the student an understanding of the fundamental construction and mechanical functioning of his body
5. To develop in the individual a pride in his physical well-being.

GIRLS' OR WOMEN'S PROGRAM. The objectives of the boys' program are equally applicable to the girl's. In addition to them one might also find the girls striving to accomplish the following:

1. Reapportion one's measurements
2. Change one's weight status
3. Firm-up slack or loose portions of the body

15 Sidney Calvin, "Effects of Progressive Resistance Exercises on the Motor Coordination of Boys," *Research Quarterly,* Vol. 30, No. 4 (December 1959), pp. 387-98.
16 Jack R. Leighton, "Weightlifting and Physical Fitness," *Strength and Health* (July 1957), pp. 30, 56 and 57.

4. Strengthen weak areas
5. Improve general body condition

Generally speaking, the aim of both groups is the improvement of one's physical appearance and condition. This, of course, is motivated by a desire to better one's social status and social relations. The students feel these will be accomplished through such improvement in condition.

PLACE OF WEIGHT TRAINING IN THE EDUCATIONAL PROGRAM. In looking over the purposes or objectives of education in general, as formulated by various commissions, one will note that health and physical fitness have ranked first or quite high among them. Present-day studies in the medical field are allying health and physical fitness more closely all the time.[17] And, since progressive weight training contributes so positively to physical fitness, it certainly has its justification for being included in the educational program.

While weight training makes such a positive contribution to physical fitness and certainly justifies being included in the educational program, one must be careful not to go so far in its acceptance that one considers progressive weight training and physical education synonymous. This has been done in some instances by over-zealous proponents of the activity. The physical activities, i.e., tumbling, apparatus work, swimming, football, basketball, etc., are the tools of the physical education profession. It is through the teaching of these that the purposes of physical education are accomplished. Progressive weight training is one of these tools and contributes to the development of some of the objectives of physical education. Considered as such, it is not a panacea or a substitute for all activities.

PROGRESSIVE WEIGHT TRAINING AS A CARRY-OVER ACTIVITY. As an activity with carry-over value into adult life, progressive weight training has one of its greatest values. Here is a method of attaining and/or maintaining good physical condition that is adaptable to meet the needs of all. No other activity offers resistance to the working of the muscles that is so constant. The resistance of the weight (iron) is not subject to change, whereas the activity of many of our competitive sports require action that varies from a quick violent expenditure to little or no expenditure of energy. No other activity can offer such a gradual change in activity resistance. The weights come in denominations as small as $1\frac{1}{4}$ lbs. which permits changes on the bar of as little as $2\frac{1}{2}$ lbs. ($1\frac{1}{4}$ lbs. to each side). The speed or cadence of exercise performance is from slow to moderate. All these factors make this activity one of the most suitable for men and women, in varying stages of condition, of varying ages, and in all walks of life.

17 "We Need Exercise," *Archives of Physical Medicine and Rehabilitation*, Vol. 40, No. 9 (September 1959), p. 406.

Fig. 1—3. Home basement gym.

Fig. 1—4. Dr. Harold Stevens.

There are several ways in which this activity may be pursued in after-school years. One of these is in the weight room of the local Y. M. C. A. or private athletic club. A second would be working out at one of the many health studios that have sprung up throughout the country. Most of these studios are well kept and are equipped with excellent exercise apparatus. The social value of exercising with others is one of the features of working out at a club or a studio. A third possibility is the personal possession of some weight equipment and exercising in one's own home. A person might set up his or her own home gym similar to the one shown in Fig. 1–3, or possess one adjustable barbell that he rolls out from beneath his bed for an exercise period every other night. More and more, people are turning to progressive weight training as a means of keeping in good physical condition, as has Dr. Harold K. Stevens, Chairman of the Department of Speech at Eastern Washington College of Education, shown in Fig. 1–4.

2

Facilities and Equipment

Facilities for conducting a course in progressive weight training need not be as extensive or elaborate as is required for other activities. A large floor space, such as is needed for some individual and team sports, is not required to teach an average-size class of 25 to 35 students; nor is extensive equipment necessary. One factor, however, is essential and that is cleanliness. The lack of it in the weight rooms of many gymnasiums has been a deterring factor in the growth in popularity of weight training. Often the weight equipment was placed in one of the more remote and inaccessible rooms in the building with a result that the room was not too often used and seldom cleaned.

The health studios that have appeared throughout the country have emphasized this factor of cleanliness to a great extent. Many studio floors are carpeted; the walls support full-length mirrors; the equipment is chromed; and all items are kept immaculately clean. This adds greatly to the attractiveness of the studios and aids in attracting clientele. Now the writer is not implying that all of this is necessary in a school situation, but only that the facility should be kept clean and racks and cabinets made available for storing equipment that is not being used.

TEACHING STATION

Any room having approximately 900 square feet of floor space and a ceiling 10 feet high will suffice for an average-size class. A room in the shape of a square will provide possibilities for greater space utilization. However, an oblong room approximately 45 feet by 20 feet is adequate. It is desirable to have the room free of obstacles such as pillars and protruding corners, but if they exist, one can arrange the equipment and exercise area around them. It is also desirable, since the floor must support much weight and will be subject to the dropping of weight, to have this room either on the main or lower floor of the building where a considerable amount of floor support exists. Upstairs is satisfactory, provided there is sufficient floor support. Obviously it is not wise to have classrooms or offices located

15

beneath the weight room. A desirable adjunct to the room is a fan that can rapidly exhaust the air from the room to the outside.

The floor of any room where weights are to be lifted should be covered with a plank flooring for protection. If the floor is concrete, a planking of two by eight's or two by ten's laid over stringers of one by four's makes a good covering and provides a spring quality to the floor. The one by four's should be spaced approximately 12 to 16 inches apart, and the planking laid edge to edge. The spring quality actually aids in exercises where the weight is returned to the floor in the execution of each repetition. It provides a slight boost to the upward movement of the weight. In rooms having wood floors supported on cross-beams or studding, this extra spring element is not necessary since the wood floor will provide the added spring. The wood floor should be covered with a plank flooring, however, to provide protection from the weights. In this case the planks may be laid edge to edge directly over the wood floor and held together by two strips of one by four's placed on top of the planks at the outer edges. The planks and stringers in both platforms are held together with counter-sunk wood screws. It is not necessary to cover the entire floor area with planking—only the area where the actual lifting of weights takes place.

FIXED EQUIPMENT

Because of their nature or to provide maximum safety, the items listed here as fixed equipment should be fastened either to the floor or to the wall or similar support, depending upon the piece of equipment. Minimal fixed equipment necessary for the conduct of the weight training programs advocated in this book includes a rack or cabinet for bars and barbell plates, a rack or cabinet for dumbbells, a regular or multipurpose bench, a wrist-roll machine for the boys' or men's program, and an additional inclined bench (see Fig. 3–27) and a lat machine (see Fig. 3–22) for the girls' or women's program. The wrist-roll machine (see Fig. 3–17) is not used in the girls' or women's program, and the last items listed are not absolutely necessary since substitute exercises without these pieces of equipment will be presented in the two programs.

PLATE CABINET AND RACK. There are two possibilities for plate racks: one in the form of a cabinet for use in rooms that accommodate several different activities or, for some reason or another, must be left open; and the other in the form of an open rack for rooms used only for weight training and which may be locked when not in use. The cabinet provides a storage space that may be closed and locked when not in use. Bars, including collars and sleeves, may be stored in the lower compartment. The locked cabinet and locked room are stressed for two reasons: (1) to prevent a novice from injuring himself by weight straining (as described in Chapter 1); and (2) to lessen the possibility of losing movable equipment.

Fig. 2—1. Barbell plate racks.

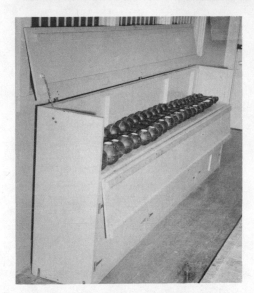

Fig. 2—2. Dumbbell racks.

Fig. 2—3. Barbell racks.

DUMBBELL CABINET AND RACK.   For the same reasons given above, there is the dumbbell cabinet that may be locked, and the open dumbbell rack. Metal shoes and other movable equipment can be stored in the lower compartments of the dumbbell cabinet.

BARBELL STORAGE.   When the bars are broken down, i.e., the plates are removed from them, they can be stored in the plate cabinet or in a separate rack. When barbells of a fixed weight are used, or when for some reason it is not desirable to break the barbell down after each use, they can be stored conveniently in racks of the type shown in Fig. 2–3. Racks or cabinets of any of these types can be made in an industrial arts shop, and some may be purchased.

OPTIONAL EQUIPMENT.   Items of equipment that enhance the exercise possibilities of the weight room are available from barbell and gymnasium equipment manufacturing companies.

MOVABLE EQUIPMENT

This equipment is of such a nature that it can either be grasped by the hand or attached to some segment of the body and moved about the body in the performance of an exercise. Weight training and lifting differ from the apparatus work in gymnastics in that the apparatus moves about the body, instead of the body moving about the apparatus.

BARBELL.   This is a round steel bar, usually 5 feet in length and approximately $1\frac{1}{16}$ inches in diameter, having inside and outside collars, a revolving sleeve, and plates of various weight denominations at each end. The bar with collars and sleeve, but minus the plates, usually weighs about 25 pounds. When the plates are added, the weight of the bar can be increased by denominations as small as $2\frac{1}{2}$ pounds up to a total of 300 pounds or more. The plates that attach to each end of the bar come in denominations of $1\frac{1}{4}$, $2\frac{1}{2}$, 5, 10, $12\frac{1}{2}$, 20, 25, and 50 pounds. When calculating the weight of a barbell, one must always remember to include the weight of the bar in with the weight of the plates. The sleeve that fits over the bar is usually knurled (roughened) for a more sure grip.

Fig. 2—4.   Barbell.

The barbell used for official weight lifting competition is seven feet in length, is equipped with a revolving sleeve on each end of the bar for ease of turning, is precision machined, and has the heavier plates in weight denominations of 45 and 35 pounds.

DUMBBELL.   Roughly speaking, this is a short-handled (12–18 inches) barbell and suited for one-arm lifting (particularly if it is of the adjustable type), whereas the barbell is suited for two-arm lifting. However, most dumbbells found in gymnasiums are of the solid cast-iron type and are in weight denominations varying from 1 lb. up to 100 lbs. or more. The weight denominations most commonly used are: 5, 10, 15, 20, 25, 30, 35, 40, 45, and 50 lbs. Dumbbells are usually obtained in pairs. The solid dumbbells of 25 lbs. and greater should have a steel handle to minimize breakage.

Fig. 2—5.   Solid iron dumbbells.

KETTLEBELL.   This type of weight is not often seen in modern gymnasiums. It is usually a round weight with a handle attached for one-arm lifting and may be either solid or adjustable.

METAL SHOE.   This is a shoe of either cast iron or aluminum and may be fastened to the bottom of the foot by straps in a manner similar to fastening on a roller or ice skate. The cast-iron shoe weighs approximately 5 lbs. while the aluminum shoe weighs approximately 2½ lbs. There is a hole running laterally through each shoe where an adjustable dumbbell handle may be placed and weights then added to the handle in any of the denominations listed for barbell plates. These are, of course, held on the bar

Fig. 2—6.   Kettlebell.

Fig. 2—7.   Metal shoes.

through the use of outside collars. In this way, weights may be used by the legs just as dumbbells are used by the arms, thus adding a variety of exercise possibilities.

RECOMMENDED MINIMAL EQUIPMENT FOR CLASSES

The following listed equipment is considered minimal for a class in progressive weight training of from 24 to 32 students. For boys' or men's classes larger than this, one bar and approximately one hundred pounds of plates should be added for each additional three or four students. For girls' or women's classes larger than this, one pair of five-pound dumbbells and one pair of metal shoes should be added for each additional two students.

BOYS' OR MEN'S PROGRAM

Fixed Equipment

Plate and bar rack or cabinet	1	Regular or multipurpose bench	2
Dumbbell rack or cabinet	1	Wrist-roll machine	1

Movable Equipment

Bars, barbell, with collars and sleeve......8

Plates for barbell:

Lbs.	No.	Lbs.	No.
25	12	10	16
20	12	5	16
12½	12	2½	16

Dumbbells, solid:

Lbs.	Pairs	Lbs.	Pairs
50	1	15	2
35	1	10	3
25	3	5	2
20	2		

GIRLS' OR WOMEN'S PROGRAM

Fixed Equipment

Plate and bar rack or cabinet	1	Inclined bench	1
Dumbbell rack or cabinet	1	Lat machine	1
Regular or multipurpose bench	2		

Movable Equipment

Bars, barbell, with collars and sleeve......4

Plates for barbell:

Lbs.	No.	Lbs.	No.
10	4	2½	8
5	8	1¼	8

Dumbbells, solid:

Lbs.	Pairs	Lbs.	Pairs
10	4	3	2
5	8		

Metal shoes:

Lbs.	Pairs	Lbs.	Pairs
5	6	2½	6

Bars, dumbbell, with collars......6

In setting up weight-training programs in the school, there is no reason why both boys and girls cannot use the same facility and equipment but at different times, thereby eliminating considerable duplication.

ARRANGEMENT OF EQUIPMENT FOR CLASS INSTRUCTION

In a square room, the platforms upon which the lifting takes place, should be constructed adjacent to the walls and extending into the room approximately eight to ten feet. Individual lifting stations separated at approximately seven to ten feet may then be established around the room. Bars and plates may be placed on racks next to the walls when not in use. Directly above this equipment and fastened to the wall should be a large mirror, approximately three feet high and four feet long. Although not a necessity, the mirror will provide the student with a means of observing his own body movement and the working of the muscles that are used in the performance of each exercise, an important aspect of the weight training program. Benches, dumbbell racks and pieces of special equipment can be conveniently located in the center of the room.

In an oblong room, the cabinets or racks should be placed along one wall so that a maximum of floor space can be utilized. The racks should be within easy access of the students using the equipment. The platform will cover most of the remaining floor space. For the boys' or men's program, all bars should be placed on the platform parallel to one another and parallel with the smaller dimension of the room. This provides for maximum utilization of space and lessens the possibility of students interfering with one another during the performance of their exercises. To specify the floor placement of these bars, crosses can be painted on the wood platform and the bars lined up on these crosses. As there will be three or four students using each bar and only one working with the bar at any one time, the remaining three should be nearby but out of the exercise area and on the side of the room opposite the weight cabinets or racks. The fixed exercise equipment should be fastened to the wood platform near the ends so as to

Fig. 2—8. Boy's weight training class, Eastern Washington College of Education.

Fig. 2—9. Girl's weight training class.

minimize interference with the exercise area and also near the movable equipment that will be used with it.

Much of what has been said above is also applicable to an arrangement of a program for girls except, of course, that the long bar or barbell is not used in a majority of the exercises of the girls' or women's program. In an oblong room, it is well to group the girls so that those using dumbbells and barbells are at one end of the room and those using the metal shoes are at the other.

CARE OF EQUIPMENT

Weight-training equipment should practically never wear out and, if given proper care, should last indefinitely from generation to generation. This fact helps to make the activity one of the cheapest, in terms of operating expense, that one can have.

Care should be taken to see that the inside collars of the barbells are always tight and that the student uses equal care in determining that the outside collars are always on and tight. The bars may be dropped without injury to the equipment but should never be dropped on one end, as this can bend the bar. Dumbbells should not be dropped since they are usually constructed of cast iron which may break by dropping. Of course, no equipment should be dropped, except in the case of an emergency. Such a situation usually occurs in weight-lifting competition where a weight being lifted is too heavy to hold and the lifter steps out from beneath it to prevent a chance of strain or injury.

There should be a designated space where each piece of equipment is placed when the user has finished with it. When an instructor has several classes in weight training follow immediately upon one another, he may wish to have the first class set the equipment out and the last class return it to its proper space, thus giving him more actual instruction time.

All equipment should be dusted frequently and constantly checked for damage. Any damage found should be repaired immediately and not be allowed to become extensive.

The floors should be dusted and the wood platform mopped daily as students will be reclining here while performing exercises as well as walking on them. Mats provide a softer substance upon which to recline but are not recommended here because of the constant walking about that takes place during an exercise period and the poor footing they provide.

3

Exercise Programs

An exercise program is a sequence of exercises (in this book, progressive weight-training exercises) designed to strengthen and develop certain muscle groups of the body. The specific exercises included and the sequence in which these exercises are performed will depend upon the purposes the program is to accomplish. The program of a man having no previous exercise experience will certainly differ from that of an athlete striving to increase his running speed in the 100-yard dash. The novice will be using a program of exercises designed to provide him with increased strength and development in all the major muscle groups of the body, whereas the sprinter will be concentrating on exercises designed to strengthen the muscles used in running. The first program is one of general body development; the second is one of specialization. This chapter deals only with programs of the first type, general body development. Chapter 6 deals with programs of exercise specialization.

There are certain exercise and lifting fundamentals with which the novice should be familiar before undertaking his first progressive weight-training exercise. These fundamentals include such matters as: the method of raising a heavy object from the floor, of moving it about; the various grips employed in grasping a bar; the method of breathing while exercising; and the importance of form in the performance of each exercise. A knowledge and mastery of the first two can save the exerciser from undue strain and/or possible injury. Knowledge of and attention to the latter will help him derive the maximum benefit from the performance of each exercise.

PRINCIPLES OF MOVING A WEIGHT

The quadriceps muscles of the front of the thigh extend the leg at the knee joint. The hamstring muscles of the back of the thigh aid in extending the leg at the hip joint. In performing these two functions, these muscle groups aid in straightening the body to an upright position. This straightening of the body, and particularly the extension of these segments, is a requisite for the execution of any lifting, pushing, or pulling movement involving the use of the legs. To obtain the maximum effort from these muscle groups in the extension movements, the segments of the body should be placed in a near-extended position; i.e., the angles at the hip and knee joints should be nearly equal to, or greater than, right angles. The back should be straight, not rounded, and at an angle of approximately 45 degrees to the floor. Any lifting, pushing, or pulling movement involving the legs and back should be performed from this position, not from a straight-legged, round-backed position or from the position of a deep squat with the hips and/or knees fully flexed.

The straight-back position offers several advantages in lifting. It places the back muscles in a contracted condition, lessening the possibility of back strain; and it reduces the sag of the abdominal muscles, giving more support to the visceral organs. This helps to reduce the possibility of abdominal rupture.

The use of the deep squat as a lifting or exercise position has been subject to criticism for some time. In addition to being a position of poor leverage, it tends to place undue stress upon the knee joint and its ligaments, subjecting them to possible injury. Lowman and Young [1] stress the avoidance of exercises utilizing this position, stating that they contribute to the production of chronic synovitis, which is similar to, but more exaggerated than, the condition known as a football knee. For these reasons, the full squat is not advocated as a developmental exercise or exercise position in this book. However, this position is used extensively in competitive weight lifting and will be described as a lifting position in that section.

METHODS OF MOVING A WEIGHT

PUSHING. Place the hands or shoulder or both against the object and lean in the direction of the movement that is to take place. Whenever feasible, the force applied to the object should be squarely in the direction the object is expected to move. Thus, the more direct the lean, up to a point of convenience, the more efficient the pushing position. The back should be straight and the position of the legs should be one of near-extension and rapid recovery as the movement takes place.

PULLING. Grasp the object with the hands and lean away from it and in the line of direction in which the movement is to take place. Here, also, the more direct the lean, up to a point of convenience, the more efficient the pulling position. Here, again, the back should be straight and the position of the legs should be one of near-extension and rapid recovery as the movement takes place.

LIFTING. The object should be near the center of gravity of the person doing the lifting. In lifting a barbell, the individual should stand directly behind the bar. The feet should be on an imaginary line parallel with the long axis of the bar. The bar should be close to the ankles. The individual

Fig. 3—1. Methods of pushing, pulling and lifting.

should bend at the knees and hips keeping the back in a near-erect (approximately 45 degrees to the floor) position, and grasp the bar on the knurlings
(the roughened areas for gripping). He should then extend the legs and
assume an erect posture, bringing the bar to the thighs. If the weight is to
come to rest at the chest, it should be brought directly upward from the
floor in an explosive movement (degree of explosiveness is dependent upon
the amount of weight being lifted) to a position approximately chest high.
The elbows should then be thrust forward under the bar to a position in
front of it. At the same time, a slight dip is taken with the legs. The over-
grip grasp (explanation following) is used in this lift to the chest.

To place the weight behind the neck, the bar is pushed directly upward
with the strength of the arms and the assist of a slight upward thrust from
the legs, following a slight dip. Then in guiding the weight to a position
on the shoulders behind the neck, the head and shoulders are thrust forward
slightly. This same technique is used in removing the weight from the
shoulders to the chest except, of course, that the head and shoulders are
moved backward instead of forward in lowering the weight back to the
chest. From here the weight is returned toward the floor by raising the
elbows behind the bar and lowering the hands to the thighs. The form in
returning the weight from the thighs to the floor is the same as that used
in raising it, except that the movement is reversed.

METHODS OF GRASPING A WEIGHT

UNDER-GRIP. With this grip, the fingers encircle the bar from beneath
with the palms of the hands up and the thumbs encircling the bar from
above. This grip is used primarily in exercises for the biceps and other
muscles of the front of the upper arm where the bar is brought from the
thighs to the shoulders and returned. It is not used in lifting a weight overhead.

OVER-GRIP. This is the grip used for all overhead lifts. It is the opposite of the under-grip in that the fingers encircle the bar from above with the palms of the hands down toward the floor. Here, the thumbs encircle the bar from beneath.

REVERSE-GRIP. This grip is used in the lifting of very heavy weights, usually from the floor to the thighs. The muscles of the forearms are not as strong as those of the legs and hips, and the weight will tend to roll out of the fingers when either the under- or over-grips are employed. With the reverse-grip, one hand grasps the bar in the under-grip position and the other hand grasps it in the over-grip position. This tends to keep the bar from rolling out of the fingers.

Fig. 3—2. Methods of grasping a barbell.

METHOD OF BREATHING DURING EXERCISE

The method of breathing during exercise is an important aspect of the progressive weight training program. If one has the occasion to visit a rather crowded weight studio where all are engaged in exercise performance, he might conclude that it is a very important aspect, indeed, from all the huffing and puffing that is so clearly heard.

In lifting a very heavy weight, such as in a competitive overhead lift, a deep breath is taken just prior to the lift and held during the execution stage of the lift. The breath is released when the lift is completed. In competition lifting, the lifter may take in and release a succession of deep breaths while getting himself set to lift the weight. The purpose of these is primarily psychological.

In weight training, where the amount of weight handled is somewhat below the individual's maximum, this breath-holding is not necessary. For the performance of the exercises advocated in this book, it is recommended that the exerciser breathe throughout the performance of all repetitions of each exercise; inhaling or breathing in during the exertion phase (while the weight is being raised) and exhaling or breathing out during the relaxation phase (while the weight is being lowered).

IMPORTANCE OF FORM DURING EXERCISE

The reader will note the rather detailed description of the manner of performing each of the exercises in the programs that follow. It is highly important that each exercise be performed in exactly the manner stated. Each exercise is designed to develop a specific muscle or group of muscles. The exercises are so designed that, for the most part, all extraneous movements involving other muscles or groups are eliminated and the work is concentrated on the one specific muscle or muscle group. Deviation from the prescribed method of performance may permit the handling of more weight in the exercise in some cases, but it also brings in other muscles or groups to handle the increased weight and may actually detract from the amount of resistance afforded the desired muscle group. In addition, deviation can cause muscular strain in the other areas.

As mentioned in Chapter 1, the flexibility or range of movement at a joint depends upon the movement pattern set at any particular joint. To develop full flexibility at a specific joint, the exercise should take the segment through the full range of movement at that joint—for example, from full extension (arms completely straightened) to full flexion (arms completely bent) at the elbow joint in the performance of the two-arms curl. This will eliminate a shortening of the range of movement and development of a "muscle-bound" condition. The full range of movement will be stressed for certain exercises.

Now, the adverse effect of the term "muscle-bound" and the emphasis that flexibility has received through the published results of the Kraus-Weber tests referred to in Chapter 1 have caused us to consider the proposition that since possessing a certain amount of flexibility is good, possessing a great degree of it in all joints of the body should be better. This is not necessarily the case. For instance, a loose knee in either a football player or a basketball player is not necessarily desirable as it is likely to predispose him to injury. This might also be true of the ankle. After all, coaches have, for years, taped the ankles of football and basketball players in an effort to prevent injury. It is also conceivable that extreme flexibility or looseness at the knee and ankle joints might be a detriment in the performance of a highly specialized skill such as field-goal and point-after-touchdown kicking in football. After all, the less the degree of extraneous movement at these two joints, the less the chance of deviation from the line of direction of the foot's pendulum swing as it moves to meet the ball and the greater the chance for a more accurate kick. The athletic coach should study his sport rather closely and adapt his exercises accordingly.

In accordance with these various reasons, movements of full and restricted range of motion will be used in the exercises that follow. There is a specific reason for the method of performance advocated for each exercise; it should be understood and the method adhered to closely.

EXERCISE PROGRAM FOR BOYS AND MEN

The following pages present fifteen fundamental exercises for a beginning program or class in progressive weight training for boys and men. These are to be followed in the approximate order presented. Deviation from this order will be discussed in Chapter 4.

1. TWO-ARMS CURL WITH BARBELL

Fig. 3—3. Two-arms curl with barbell.

Starting position: Erect standing position with feet comfortably apart, the arms fully extended at sides, and the hands grasping the bar in front of the body with the under-grip, approximately shoulder-width apart.

Movement: (1) Bend the arms at the elbows and bring the bar, in an arc, to the chest. (2) Return to starting position.

Resistance: 25-50 lbs., or approximately one-quarter body weight.

Starting repetitions: 5.

Cadence: Slow.

Caution: Do not bend backward at the waist or move the elbows back from the sides of the body. The arms should be fully extended at the completion of movement 2.

Principal muscles affected: Biceps and brachialis of the front of the upper arm.

2. PRESS BEHIND NECK WITH BARBELL

Starting position: Erect standing position with the feet comfortably apart, the bar placed behind the neck and resting on the shoulders, hands grasping the bar out near the inside collars with the over-grip.

Movement: (1) Extend the arms upward pushing the bar to arm's length overhead. (2) Return to starting position.

Resistance: 40-75 lbs., or approximately one-half body weight.

Fig. 3—4. Press behind neck with barbell.

Starting repetitions: 5.

Cadence: Slow.

Caution: Do not bend the knees or bend backward at the waist, thereby using the legs and back to assist with the lift. The arms should be completely extended at the completion of movement 1 and the bar should be returned to the shoulders at the completion of movement 2.

Principal muscles affected: Triceps of the back of the upper arm, deltoid of the shoulder, and trapezius of the upper back.

3. ROWING MOTION WITH BARBELL

Fig. 3—5. Rowing motion with barbell.

Starting position: Standing position with the body inclined forward 90 degrees at the hips, the knees slightly bent, feet comfortably apart, the back flat with the abdominal muscles tensed, and the arms extended downward with the hands grasping the bar, which is on the floor, with the over-grip about shoulder-width apart.

Movement: (1) Flex the arms and extend the elbows to the sides of the body at shoulder level bringing the bar to the chest. (2) Return to starting position.

Resistance: 40-75 lbs., or approximately one-half body weight.

Starting repetitions: 5.

Cadence: Moderate.

Caution: The back should be flat, not rounded, with the abdominal muscles tensed, and should not be moved upward and downward during performance of the exercise. The elbows should be extended out to the sides at shoulder level with the bar coming to the chest, and not back along the sides of the body bringing the bar to the abdomen. The arms should be fully extended at the completion of movement 2.

Principal muscles affected: Trapezius and rhomboid major and minor of the upper back, deltoid of the shoulder, and biceps and brachialis of the front of the upper arm.

4. SHOULDER SHRUG WITH BARBELL

Fig. 3—6.   Shoulder shrug with barbell.

Starting position: Erect standing position with feet comfortably apart, the arms at sides, hands grasping the bar in front of the body out near the inside collars with the over-grip.

Movement: (1) Lift the shoulders upward toward the ears as far as possible. (2) Return to starting position.

Resistance: 40-75 lbs., or approximately one-half body weight.

Starting repetitions: 10.

Cadence: Slow.

Caution: Keep the arms straight; do not bend the elbows during the movement. Lift the shoulders upward as far as possible.

Principal muscles affected: Trapezius and levator scapulae of the upper back and neck.

5. STRADDLE LIFT WITH BARBELL

Fig. 3—7. Straddle lift with barbell.

Starting position: Erect standing position with feet comfortably apart. The bar is held between the legs at crotch height with the reverse grip, one arm being in front of the body and the other behind it. The bar should be held at a right angle to an imaginary line connecting the two feet.

Movement: (1) Perform a half squat or knee bend so that the angle at the knee joint approaches a right angle. (2) Return to starting position.

Resistance: 40-75 lbs., or approximately one-half body weight.

Starting repetitions: 10; five with the right arm in front and the left arm behind, and five with the left arm in front and the right arm behind. Holding a weight in this position places a twist on the spine and more pull upon one side of the back than on the other. Reversing the arm positions half way through the exercise repetitions tends to equalize this pull upon the back muscles.

Cadence: Slow.

Caution: There may be a tendency to bend forward at the hips during the performance of this exercise, thus placing a greater share of the load upon the lower back muscles. This is usually due to one of two things: either (1) the feet are not lined up side to side; i.e., one foot may be advanced farther than the other, causing the bar not to be held at a right angle to the body; or (2) the individual may not have sufficient flexibility in the ankle joint to keep his feet flat on the floor for balance during the performance of the exercise. In the first instance, the form should be corrected; in the second, some object, such as a barbell plate, should be placed under the heels raising them off the floor. This will aid in maintaining balance. The knees should not be bent to less than a right angle and the back should be kept erect throughout the performance of the exercise.

Principal muscles affected: Quadriceps femoris (rectus femoris, vastus lateralis, vastus intermedius, vastus medialis) of the front of the thigh or upper leg, hamstrings (biceps femoris, semitendinosus, semimembranosus) of the back of the thigh, and the gluteus maximus of the hip.

6. RISE ON TOES WITH BARBELL

Fig. 3—8.   Rise on toes with barbell.

Starting position: Erect standing position with feet comfortably apart, the bar placed behind the neck and resting on the shoulders, hands grasping the bar out near the inside collars with the over-grip.

Movement: (1) Rise up on the balls of feet and toes. (2) Return to starting position.

Resistance: 40-75 lbs., or approximately one-half body weight.

Starting repetitions: 20; ten with the toes pointed in, and ten with the toes pointed out. The calf or gastrocnemius muscle is two-headed, one being on the medial side of the back of the lower leg and the other on the lateral side. Both heads of the muscle receive their optimum development when the exercise is performed in this manner.

Cadence: Slow.

Caution: The back should remain erect and the knees locked throughout performance of the exercise. The individual should rise upward as far as possible, and the feet should have a definite inward or outward slant, depending on the phase of the exercise. The placing of a board beneath the balls of the feet is not recommended.

Principal muscles affected: Calf muscles (gastrocnemius and soleus) of the back of the lower leg.

7. REVERSE CURL WITH BARBELL

Fig. 3—9. Reverse curl with barbell.

Exercise: Same as the two-arms curl (see page 28), except that the bar is grasped with the over-grip and at slightly less than shoulder-width apart. The elbows should be kept close to the sides of the body throughout the movement and the wrists should be extended at the start to provide maximum wrist strength to the exercise.

Principal muscles affected: Biceps and brachialis of the front of the upper arm and brachioradialis of the forearm.

8. SIDE BEND WITH DUMBBELL

Fig. 3—10. Side bend with dumbbell.

Starting position: Erect standing position with feet comfortably apart and the arms at the sides of the body, one hand grasping a dumbbell.

Movement: Bend to the dumbbell side of the body as far as possible. (1) Bend to the opposite side as far as possible. (2) Return to the position specified for the start of count 1.

Resistance: 10-25 lbs.

Starting repetitions: 20; ten with the dumbbell held in the right hand, and ten with the dumbbell held in the left hand.

Cadence: Moderate.

Caution: The knees should be kept locked with the legs straight, the hips locked, and all the movement performed at the waist. The bending should be directly sideward and not slightly forward.

Principal muscles affected: External and internal oblique muscles at the sides of the waist.

9. HALF-SQUAT WITH BARBELL

Fig. 3—11. Half-squat with barbell.

Starting position: Erect standing position with feet comfortably apart, the bar placed behind the neck and resting on the shoulders, hands grasping the bar out near the inside collars with the over-grip.

Movement: (1) Perform a half squat or knee bend so that the angle at the knee joint approaches a right angle. (2) Return to starting position.

Resistance: 40-75 lbs., or approximately one-half body weight.

Starting repetitions: 10.

Cadence: Moderate.

Caution: The back should remain straight and upright during performance of the exercise. If the individual has a tendency to bend forward from the hips, thus placing a greater share of the load on his lower back muscles, or if he rises up on his toes and has trouble balancing; he probably lacks sufficient flexibility in the ankle joint to keep his feet flat on the floor during the performance of the exercise. Placing a barbell plate or piece of wood under the heels will help overcome this difficulty. The knees should not be bent to less than a right angle during the exercise performance.

Principal muscles affected: Quadriceps femoris (rectus femoris, vastus lateralis, vastus intermedius, vastus medialis) of the front of the upper leg or thigh, hamstrings (biceps femoris, semitendinosus, semimembranosus) of the back of the upper leg, and gluteus maximus of the hip.

10. TWO-ARMS PRESS WITH BARBELL

Fig. 3—12. Two-arms press with barbell.

Starting position: Erect standing position with feet comfortably apart, the bar held at the chest with the hands about shoulder-width apart and with the over-grip, elbows bent and extended forward of bar.

Movement: (1) Extend the arms, pushing bar upward to arm's length overhead. (2) Return to starting position.

Resistance: 40-75 lbs., or approximately one-half body weight.

Starting repetitions: 5.

Cadence: Slow.

Caution: Do not bend the knees or bend backward at the waist, thereby using the legs and back to assist with the lift. The arms should be completely extended at the completion of movement 1 and the bar returned to the chest at the completion of movement 2.

Principal muscles affected: Triceps of the back of the upper arm and deltoid of the shoulder.

11. STIFF-LEGGED DEAD LIFT WITH BARBELL

Fig. 3—13. Stiff-legged dead lift with barbell.

Starting position: Standing position, feet together and knees locked with legs straight, body bent forward at the hips, the abdominal muscles tensed, hands grasping bar resting immediately in front of the body on the floor with the over-grip, arms straight.

Movement: (1) Come to erect standing position. (2) Return to starting position.

Resistance: 40-75 lbs., or approximately one-half body weight.

Starting repetitions: 10.

Cadence: Moderate.

Caution: The legs and arms should be kept straight throughout the exercise. The individual should come to a completely erect position during each repetition. If the individual cannot reach the floor with the barbell, he should bend his knees when he first lifts the weight from the floor; but from then on he should keep the legs straight and bend over as far as possible even though he does not reach the floor with the barbell. He will, of course, need to bend his knees when he returns the weight to the floor following the last exercise repetition.

Principal muscles affected: Hamstrings (biceps femoris, semitendinosus, semimembranosus) of the back of the upper leg, the gluteus maximus of the hip, and the spinal erector group (iliocostalis lumborum, longissimus dorsi, spinalis dorsi) of the lower back.

12. TWO-ARMS PULL-OVER WITH BARBELL

Starting position: Lying position with back on the floor, legs flexed at the hips so that the knees are above the chest. The lower legs extend

Fig. 3—14.　Two-arms pull-over with barbell.

parallel with the floor from flexed knees and are crossed at the ankles. The arms are extended beyond the head, hands grasping the bar out near the inside collars with the over-grip (palms facing up in this case).

Movement: (1) Bring the bar in an arc to a position directly above the chest. (2) Return to starting position.

Resistance: 10-30 lbs. The bar weighs 25 lbs. If this is too heavy, use a dumbbell and grasp the outside of each globe end with the hands.

Starting repetitions: 10.

Cadence: Moderate.

Caution: The knees should be raised to a position above the chest. This helps to keep the lower back flat on the floor during performance of the exercise. If the legs are held straight on the floor and not raised, there is a tendency to lock the shoulders on the downward movement of the weight and lower it the final distance by arching the back. This can contribute to the development of an exaggerated curvature or arch in the lower back and a decreasing range of movement at the shoulder joint. The arms should be kept straight throughout the exercise. If the individual has a history of a previous shoulder injury, the elbows should be bent and projected directly upward and not out to the side. In this case the range of movement at the shoulder joint should be restricted.

Principal muscles affected: Latissimus dorsi of the back and pectoralis major of the chest.

13.　SIT-UP WITH DUMBBELL

Starting position: Lying position with back on the floor, legs bent at the knees and hips so that the feet are resting on the floor close to the hips and held down by an object or partner. A dumbbell is held on the chest by grasping the outside of the globe ends with the hands.

Movement: (1) Rise to a sitting position, the dumbbell coming close to the knees. (2) Return to starting position.

Resistance: 5-25 lbs.

Starting repetitions: 10.

Fig. 3—15.   Sit-up with dumb-bell.

Cadence: Moderate.

Caution: The knees should be bent, placing the feet close to the but-tocks. The weight should be placed on the chest. The rectus abdominus muscles that this exercise is designed to develop stretch from the xiphoid process of the chest to the pubic bone. It is important to note that they do not pass over the hip joint and hence have nothing to do with bend-ing the body forward at the hips. This function is performed by the iliopsoas group and the rectus femoris of the quadriceps femoris group. The psoas muscles of the iliopsoas group attach to the front of the spine in the lower back, extend down through the abdominal cavity and attach to the femur bones of the upper legs.

If the legs are kept straight in performing this exercise and if the weight is placed behind the neck, a major portion of the muscle pull will be forward and upward in the lower back area of the spine, resisted by the weight behind the neck. This, as with the pull-over when performed with legs straight, can place an exaggerated arch in the lower back. Improper performance of this exercise can cause a shortening of the iliopsoas muscle group, thus fixing this lower-back curvature. The plac-ing of the feet near the buttocks and the dumbbell on the chest eliminates arching of the back and places the rectus abdominus muscles in a better mechanical position to assist the movement, by moving the xiphoid process closer to the pubic bone.

Principal muscles affected: Rectus abdominus of the front of the lower trunk, iliopsoas (iliacus, psoas major, psoas minor) of the lower back and upper leg, and rectus femoris of the front of the upper leg.

14. SUPINE PRESS WITH BARBELL

Starting position: Lying position with back on bench, the elbows ex-tended downward and to the sides, the bar held on the chest by the hands with the over-grip and at a little more than shoulder-width apart.

Movement: (1) Push the bar upward to arm's length above the chest. (2) Return to starting position.

Resistance: 40-75 lbs., or approximately one-half body weight.

Fig. 3—16. Supine press with barbell.

Starting repetitions: 5.

Cadence: Slow.

Caution: Rising upon the shoulders, back of neck, and feet as a means of assisting the lifting of the weight should not be permitted. When this happens, the weight being used is usually too heavy. The bar should be lowered until it touches the chest and raised upward until the arms are straight in each exercise repetition.

Principal muscles affected: Triceps of the back of the upper arm, pectoralis major of the front of the chest and deltoid of the shoulder.

15. WRIST ROLL WITH WRIST-ROLL MACHINE OR STICK AND ROPE

Starting position: Erect standing position facing wrist-roll machine, hands grasping roller with the over-grip, arms straight.

Movement: (1) Roll the weight up to the top with wrist flexion movements. (2) Return the weight to the floor. (3) Roll the weight to the top with wrist extension movements. (4) Return the weight to the floor.

Resistance: 10-25 lbs.

Starting repetitions: 5. The four parts described under movement constitute one repetition.

Cadence: Moderate.

Caution: The arms should be kept straight throughout movement and not allowed to bend at the elbows.

Principal muscles affected: Flexor (flexor carpi radialis, palmaris longus, flexor digitorum sublimis, etc.) and extensor (extensor carpi radialis longus, extensor digitorum communis, extensor carpi ulnaris, etc.) muscles of the forearm.

Substitution: A simple substitute for the wrist-roll machine can be made with a round stick approximately 18 inches long and 2 inches in diameter and a piece of clothesline rope approximately 8 feet in length. Bore a hole through the center diameter of the stick large enough to take the rope. Tie a knot in one end of the rope, put the other end through the hole, and pull until the knot comes in contact with the stick. The knot

Fig. 3—17. Wrist roll with wrist-roll machine.

will fasten the rope to the stick and the other end should be tied to a barbell plate. The stick is held at arm's length in front of the body and at shoulder height by the shoulder muscles while the hands roll the rope up on the stick, raising the weight.

15a. WRIST CURL WITH BARBELL

The two exercises, 15a and 15b, may be substituted for exercise number 15.

Starting position: Sitting position on bench with forearms resting on thighs, wrists extended beyond the knees and hands grasping bar with the under-grip, approximately shoulder width apart.

Fig. 3—18. Wrist curl with barbell.

Movement: Extend the hands at the wrists, lowering the bar as far as possible. (1) Flex the wrists, bringing the bar upward as far as possible. (2) Return to position described as the beginning for count 1.

Resistance: 25-45 lbs.

Starting repetitions: 10.

Cadence: Slow.

Caution: Do not move the forearms on the thighs. All movement should take place at the wrist joint.

Principal muscles affected: Flexor (flexor carpi radialis, palmaris longus, flexor digitorum sublimis, etc.) muscles of the forearm.

15b. REVERSE WRIST CURL WITH BARBELL

Fig. 3—19. Reverse wrist curl with barbell.

Exercise: Same as the wrist curl exercise, number 15a above, except that the bar is grasped with the over-grip. A lighter weight than that used for exercise 15a will probably be required for correct performance.

Principal muscles affected: Extensor (extensor carpi radialis longus, extensor digitorum communis, extensor carpi ulnaris, etc.) muscles of the forearm.

EXERCISE PROGRAM FOR GIRLS AND WOMEN

The following seventeen fundamental exercises are for a beginning program or class in progressive weight training for girls and women. These should be followed in the approximate order presented. Class deviation from this order will be discussed in Chapter 4.

1. ALTERNATE CURL WITH DUMBBELLS

Starting position: Erect standing position with the arms at sides, each hand grasping a dumbbell with the palms facing forward.

Movement: Bend the right arm at the elbow and bring the dumbbell to the right shoulder, turn the hand over so that the palm is down and

Fig. 3—20. Alternate curl with dumbbells.

lower it to the starting position. As the dumbbell in the right hand is being lowered, bring the dumbbell in the left hand to the left shoulder. Keep the arms moving alternately at the elbow joints until the prescribed number of repetitions is completed.

Resistance: 3-10 lbs. for each arm.

Starting repetitions: 5. One complete flexion and extension movement by both lower arms constitutes one repetition.

Cadence: Slow.

Caution: Do not bend backward at the waist or move the elbows back from the sides of the body. Girls may have a little difficulty coordinating the movements the first few times.

Principal muscles affected: Biceps and brachialis of the front of the upper arm.

2. ALTERNATE TRICEPS EXTENSION WITH DUMBBELLS

Starting position: Lying position with back on floor or bench and arms extended upward, hands holding dumbbells directly above the shoulders.

Movement: Bend the right arm at the elbow bringing the dumbbell to the right shoulder, then extend the lower arm until it returns to the starting position. As the dumbbell in the right hand is being extended, lower the left dumbbell to the left shoulder. Keep the arms moving alternately at the elbow joints until the prescribed number of repetitions is completed.

Resistance: 3-10 lbs. for each arm.

Starting repetitions: 5. A complete flexion and extension movement by both lower arms constitutes one repetition.

Cadence: Slow.

Fig. 3—21. Alternate triceps extension with dumbbells.

Caution: There should be no movement of the upper arm. All movement should be by the forearm at the elbow joint.

Principal muscles affected: Triceps of the back of the upper arm.

3. PULL-DOWN TO BACK OF NECK USING LAT MACHINE

Starting position: Sitting position astride bench with the arms extended directly overhead, hands grasping the bar of lat machine with the over-grip at slightly greater than shoulder-width apart.

Movement: (1) Pull the bar down to back of neck. (2) Return to starting position.

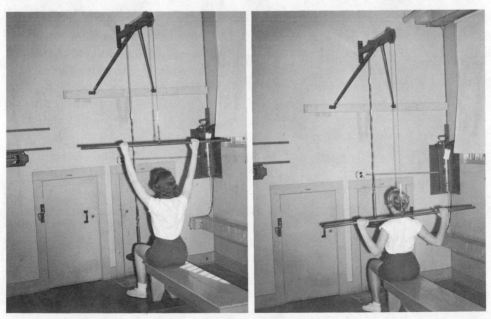

Fig. 3—22. Pull-down to back of neck, using lat machine.

Resistance: 10-25 lbs. In calculating this resistance, the weight of the lat machine bar (approximately 15 lbs.) must be subtracted from the amount of weight on the loading bar to give the actual amount of resistance. The reason for this is that the bar is attached to the cable on the opposing side to the weights and hence, is a 15 lb. assist in raising the weights. Thus to provide 10 lbs. resistance on the lat machine, one must place approximately 25 lbs. of weight on the loading bar.

Starting repetitions: 10.

Cadence: Slow.

Caution: Keep the feet out of the way of the descending weights and sit sufficiently beneath the outer pulley of the lat machine so that an erect back position can be maintained.

Principal muscles affected: Latissimus dorsi of the back, teres major and minor, rhomboid major and minor, and trapezius of the upper back, and biceps and brachialis of the front of the upper arm.

3a. SINGLE-ARM SIDE PULL-OVER WITH DUMBBELL

Fig. 3—23.   Single-arm side pull-over with dumbbell.

This exercise may be substituted for exercise 3.

Starting position: Side lying position on floor with lower arm resting on floor in front of body and upper arm extended beyond head, hand grasping dumbbell resting on floor.

Movement: (1) Raise the dumbbell upward above the shoulder and bring it down to the side of the body. (2) Return to starting position.

Resistance: 3-5 lbs.

Starting repetitions: 10, each arm.

Cadence: Slow.

Caution: Rolling onto the back is not permitted in the performance of this exercise. The arm should be kept straight and not bent at the elbow joint.

Principal muscles affected: Latissimus dorsi of the back, teres major and minor, rhomboid major and minor, and trapezius of the upper back, and deltoid of the shoulder.

4. HALF-SQUAT WITH BARBELL OR DUMBBELL

Fig. 3—24. Half-squat with dumbbell.

Starting position: Erect standing position with feet comfortably apart, heels raised and placed on piece of wood or barbell plate, the weight placed behind the neck and resting on the shoulders, hands grasping the globe ends if dumbbell is used, or the bar out near the inside collars with the over-grip.

Movement: (1) Perform a half-squat or knee bend so that the angle at the knee joint approaches a right angle. (2) Return to starting position.

Resistance: 10-30 lbs.

Starting repetitions: 10.

Cadence: Moderate.

Caution: The back should remain straight and upright during performance of the exercise. The knees should not be bent to less than a right angle during the exercise performance.

Principal muscles affected: Quadriceps femoris (rectus femoris, vastus lateralis, vastus intermedius, vastus medialis) of the front of the upper leg or thigh, hamstrings (biceps femoris, semitendinosus, semimembranosus) of the back of the upper leg, and gluteus maximus of the hip.

5. RISE ON TOES WITH BARBELL OR DUMBBELL

Starting position: Erect standing position with feet comfortably apart, the weight placed behind the neck and resting on the shoulders, hands grasping the globe ends if dumbbell is used or the bar out near the inside collars with the over-grip.

Fig. 3—25. Rise on toes with dumbbell.

Movement: (1) Rise up on the balls of feet and toes. (2) Return to starting position.

Resistance: 10-30 lbs.

Starting repetitions: 20; ten with the toes pointed in and ten with the toes pointed out. The calf or gastrocnemius muscle is two-headed, one being on the medial side of the back of the lower leg and the other on the lateral side. Both heads of the muscle receive their optimum development when the exercise is performed in this manner.

Cadence: Slow.

Caution: The back should remain erect and the knees locked throughout the performance of the exercise. The individual should rise upward as far as possible and the feet should have a definite inward or outward slant, depending on the phase of the exercise. The placing of a board beneath the balls of the feet is not recommended.

Principal muscles affected: Calf muscles (gastrocnemius and soleus) of the back of the lower leg.

6. FRONT AND LATERAL RAISE WITH DUMBBELLS

Starting position: Erect standing position with feet comfortably apart, arms at sides, and hands grasping dumbbells with the knuckles front.

Movement: (1) Raise the arms forward and upward overhead. (2) Return to starting position. (3) Turn the knuckles out and raise the arms sideward and upward overhead. (4) Return to starting position.

Fig. 3—26. Front and lateral raise with dumbbells.

Resistance: 3-5 lbs. for each arm.

Starting repetitions: 5. The four parts described under movement constitute one repetition.

Cadence: Slow.

Caution: Keep the arms straight; i.e., do not bend the elbows during the movement. All movement should take place at the shoulder joint. Swinging the dumbbells upward by extending the back should not be permitted.

Principal muscles affected: Deltoid muscles of the shoulder and trapezius of the upper back.

7. INCLINED-BENCH PRESS WITH DUMBBELLS

Starting position: Reclining position, back against inclined bench (at approximately 45 degrees), dumbbells held at shoulder height and a short distance away from the body.

Movement: (1) Extend the arms upward above the chest until the arms are straight and the dumbbells close together. (2) Return to starting position.

Resistance: 3-10 lbs. for each arm.

Starting repetitions: 5.

Cadence: Slow.

Caution: The arms should move the dumbbells directly upward over the chest and not out in front of the body. The arms should be stretched

Fig. 3—27.   Inclined-bench press with dumbbells.

backward at the shoulders during movement 2.

Principal muscles affected: Pectoralis major of the chest, triceps of the back of the upper arm, and deltoid of the shoulder.

Substitution: This exercise may be performed on a regular bench if an inclined bench is not available.

8. SIT-UP WITH DUMBBELL

Starting position: Lying position with back on the floor, legs bent at the knees and hips so that the feet are resting on the floor close to the hips and held down by an object or partner. A dumbbell is held on the upper chest by grasping the outside of the globe ends with the hands. When no weight is used, the arms may be placed at the sides of the body and raised forward during the sitting up.

Movement: (1) Rise to a sitting position, the dumbbell coming close to the knees. (2) Return to starting position.

Resistance: 0-10 lbs.

Starting repetitions: 10.

Cadence: Moderate.

Caution: The knees should be bent, placing the feet close to the hips. The weight should be placed on the chest. The rectus abdominus muscles that this exercise is designed to develop stretch from the xiphoid process of the chest to the pubic bone. It is important to note that they do not pass over the hip joint and hence have nothing to do with bending the body forward at the hips. This function is performed by the iliopsoas group and the rectus femoris of the quadriceps femoris group.

Fig. 3—28. Sit-up with dumb-bell.

The psoas muscles of the iliopsoas group attach to the front of the spine in the lower back, extend down through the abdominal cavity and attach to the femur bones of the upper legs. If the legs are kept straight in performing this exercise and if the weight is placed behind the neck, a major portion of the muscle pull will be forward and upward in the lower back area of the spine, resisted by the weight behind the neck. This, as with the pull-over when performed with legs straight, can place an exaggerated arch in the lower back. Improper performance of this exercise can cause a shortening of the iliopsoas muscle group, thus fixing this lower back curvature. The placing of the feet near the buttocks and the dumbbell on the chest eliminates this arching of the back and places the rectus abdominus muscles in a better mechanical position to assist the movement, by moving the xiphoid process closer to the pubic bone.

Principal muscles affected: Rectus abdominus of the front of the lower trunk, iliospsoas (iliacus, psoas major, psoas minor) of the lower back and upper leg, and rectus femoris of the front of the upper leg.

9. SIDE BEND WITH DUMBBELL

Starting position: Erect standing position with the feet comfortably apart and the arms at the sides of the body, one hand grasping a dumbbell.

Movement: Bend to the dumbbell side of the body as far as possible. (1) Bend to the opposite side as far as possible. (2) Return to the position specified for the start of count 1.

Resistance: 5-10 lbs.

Starting repetitions: 20; ten with the dumbbell held in the right hand and ten with the dumbbell held in the left hand.

Cadence: Moderate.

Caution: The knees should be kept locked with the legs straight, the hips locked, and all the movement performed at the waist. The bending should be directly sideward and not slightly forward.

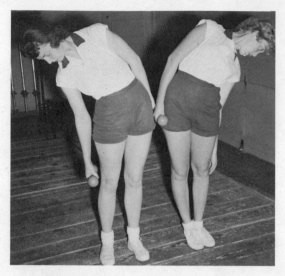

Fig. 3—29. Side bend with dumbbell.

Principal muscles affected: External and internal oblique muscles at the sides of the waist.

10. STIFF-LEGGED BEND-OVER WITH BARBELL OR DUMBBELL

Starting position: Erect standing position with feet comfortably apart, the bar placed on the shoulders behind the neck, and the hands grasping the bar near the inside collars with the over-grip or, in case a dumbbell is used, the outside of the globe ends.

Fig. 3—30. Stiff-legged bend-over with dumbbell.

Movement: (1) Bend forward at the hips as far as possible. (2) Return to starting position.

Resistance: 5-25 lbs.

Starting repetitions: 10.

Cadence: Slow.

Caution: The legs should be kept straight throughout the exercise; i.e., the knees should not be bent. The individual should keep the abdominal muscles slightly tensed during the forward movement and should return to a completely erect position during each repetition of the exercise.

Principal muscles affected: Hamstrings (biceps femoris, semitendinosus, semimembranosus) of the back of the upper leg, the gluteus maximus of the hip, and the spinal erector group (iliocostalis lumborum, longissimus dorsi, spinalis dorsi) of the lower back.

11. TWO-ARMS PULL-OVER WITH DUMBBELL

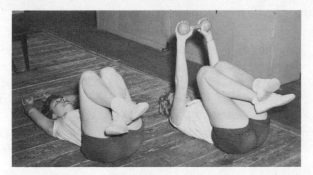

Fig. 3—31. Two-arms pull-over with dumbbell.

Starting position: Lying position with back on the floor, legs flexed at the hips so that the knees are above the chest, the lower legs extend parallel with the floor from flexed knees and are crossed at the ankles. The arms are extended beyond the head, hands grasping the outside of the globe ends of a dumbbell.

Movement: (1) Bring the dumbbell in an arc to a position directly above the chest. (2) Return to starting position.

Resistance: 3-10 lbs.

Starting repetitions: 10.

Cadence: Moderate.

Caution: The knees should be raised to a position above the chest. This helps to keep the lower back flat on the floor during the performance of the exercise. If the legs are held straight on the floor and not raised, there is a tendency to lock the shoulders on the downward movement of the weight and lower it the final distance by arching the back. This can contribute to the development of an exaggerated curvature or arch in the lower back and a decreasing range of movement at the shoulder joint. The arms should be kept straight throughout the exercise. If the individual has a history of a previous shoulder injury, the elbows should be bent and projected directly upward and not out to the side. In this case the range of movement at the shoulder joint should be restricted.

Principal muscles affected: Latissimus dorsi of the back and pectoralis major of the chest.

12. LEG PUSH-AWAYS WITH METAL SHOES

Fig. 3—32.   Leg push-aways with metal shoes.

Starting position: Lying position with back on the floor, legs flexed at the hips so that the knees are above the abdomen and flexed at the knees so that the lower legs are parallel with the floor, and with metal shoes attached to the bottom of the feet. The lower back should be flat on the floor and the arms on the floor at the sides.

Movement: (1) Extend the legs at the hips and knees as far as possible without raising the lower back from the floor. (2) Return to starting position.

Resistance: 0-5 lbs. (a 2½ lb. metal shoe attached to each foot).

Starting repetitions: 10.

Cadence: Slow.

Caution: Do not permit the legs to be extended to the point where an arch is created in the lower back. The lower back should remain in contact with the floor at all times during the exercise.

Principal muscles affected: Rectus abdominus of the front of the lower trunk. The work of these muscles is in maintaining the position of the lower back on the floor.

13. SINGLE-LEG EXTENSION WITH METAL SHOE

Starting position: Sitting position on a high bench with metal shoe attached to one foot, hands on bench at sides.

Movement: (1) Extend the lower leg at the knee joint as far as possible. (2) Return to starting position.

Resistance: 2½-5 lbs.

Starting repetitions: 10, each leg.

Cadence: Slow.

Caution: The leg should be fully extended at the knee joint during each repetition of the exercise.

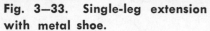

Fig. 3—33. Single-leg extension
with metal shoe.

Fig. 3—34. Single-leg back extension
with metal shoe.

Principal muscles affected: Quadriceps femoris (rectus femoris, vastus lateralis, vastus intermedius, vastus medialis) muscles of the front of the upper leg.

14. SINGLE-LEG BACK EXTENSION WITH METAL SHOE

Starting position: Erect standing position near a wall or fixed object with hands resting against it for support. Metal shoes are attached to both feet.

Movement: (1) Extend one leg backward at the hip joint as far as possible. (2) Return to starting position.

Resistance: 2½-5 lbs.

Starting repetitions: 10, each leg.

Cadence: Moderate.

Caution: The body should remain erect, not inclined forward during exercise. The leg should be moved forcibly back from the starting position and not swung like a pendulum, and should remain straight at the knee joint.

Principal muscles affected: Gluteus maximus of the hip.

15. SIDE-LYING LEG SCISSORS WITH METAL SHOE

Starting position: Lying position with left side of body on floor and metal shoe attached to right foot, which is extended to the rear of the left as far as possible and resting on the floor. The legs are straight at the knee

Fig. 3—35. Side-lying leg scissors with metal shoe.

joints. The left arm should be resting on the floor, extended beyond the head, and the right arm extended in front of the body, hand on the floor for balance.

Movement: (1) Lift the right leg and bring it forward over the left, placing the right foot on the floor as far in front of the left as possible. (2) Lift the right leg and return it to starting position.

Resistance: 2½-5 lbs.

Starting repetitions: 10, each leg. The right side of the body will recline on the floor when the left leg is performing the movement.

Cadence: Slow.

Caution: The leg performing the movement should be kept straight at the knee joint throughout the exercise and should be lifted sufficiently high above the floor to clear the opposite leg with ease.

Principal muscles affected: Abductor (tensor fasciae latae, gluteus medius, gluteus minimus, piriformis) muscles of the hip.

16. STRAIGHT-LEGGED BICYCLE WITH METAL SHOES

Starting position: Lying position with back on the floor and hips supported in the air by the hands, elbows on the floor. The legs are extended directly above the hips with metal shoes attached to the feet.

Movement: Bend the right leg at the hip, bringing the metal shoe to a position just off the floor beyond the head; then extend the leg at the hip joint, returning it to the starting position. As the right leg is being returned to the starting position, bend the left leg at the hip, bringing the metal shoe to a position just off the floor beyond the head. Keep the legs moving alternately at the hips until the prescribed number of repetitions is completed.

Resistance: 2½-5 lbs. for each leg.

Starting repetitions: 10. A complete flexion and extension movement by both legs at the hip joint constitutes one repetition.

Cadence: Moderate.

Fig. 3—36. Straight-legged bicycle with metal shoes.

Caution: The legs should be kept straight at the knee joints during the performance of the exercise. The individual should make certain of her balance before starting the scissors movement and start slowly or she might be pulled off balance by the weight of the shoes.

Principal muscles affected: Hamstrings (biceps femoris, semitendinosus, semimembranosus) of the back of the upper leg and the gluteus maximus of the hip.

17. FORWARD RAISE ON BENCH WITH DUMBBELLS

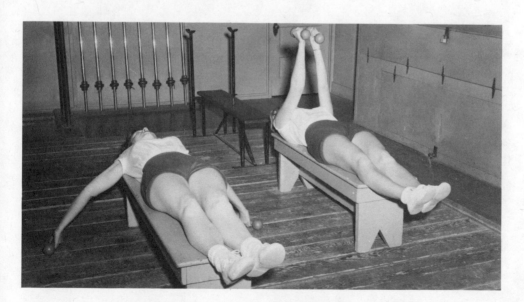

Fig. 3—37. Forward raise on bench with dumbbells.

Starting position: Lying position with back on bench, hands grasping dumbbells at arm's length directly above the shoulders.

Movement: (1) Lower the arms to the sides at shoulder level as far back and away from the body as possible. (2) Return to starting position.

Resistance: 3-5 lbs. for each arm.

Starting repetitions: 5.

Cadence: Slow.

Caution: The arms should be kept straight at the elbows and lowered as far as possible.

Principal muscles affected: Pectoralis major of the chest and deltoid of the shoulder.

4

Conduct of the
Exercise Programs

Progressive weight training is definitely an individual activity, even though it may be taught in a class or group situation. Each exercise has its purpose for the individual performing it. If all are performing the same exercise in the same manner, the exercise purpose is, of course, the same for all. It is highly important that this purpose is understood by each one.

Now, although all of the students in a school physical education class of progressive weight training may be performing the same set of exercises, which is advocated here for beginning classes, the amount of resistance used by each student will vary greatly. (This can be determined by examining the proposed approximate starting resistance advocated in Chapter 3.) In such a class, each student should understand that there is to be no competition between one another for grades or any other class reward in terms of the amount of resistance he and his neighbor are using in the performance of the same exercise. The optimum in improvement for each individual should be the major concern here. This, of course, does not rule out friendly competition between individuals of approximately the same size and strength. Such competition often adds zest to the workout.

Progressive weight training may be conducted in either a formal or an informal manner. In the formal manner, all students perform the same exercise at the same time to the count of the instructor. This method is similar to that employed in the conduct of a military-type calisthenics routine. In the informal manner of class conduct, the students progress from one exercise to the next at their own rate and perform the specified number of repetitions to their own cadence. This method aids in reducing any feeling of stiffness that is sometimes felt in formally conducted situations, and makes it possible for the instructor to move about the room, giving exercise hints where needed. The writer has employed this method a number of years for both boys and girls classes, and feels that it is considerably superior to the former. The method of class conduct advocated in this chapter will be based on this informal method.

57

BASIC EXERCISE PROGRAM

For the boy or girl who has had no previous experience in class weight training instruction, the program of exercises listed in Chapter 3 is recommended. Exercises designed to develop all of the major muscle groups of the body are included in the boys' program with repeat emphasis placed on the arm and leg groups. All exercises should be performed in the order listed with the exception of the supine press and wrist roll which may be worked into the routine whenever the particular piece of apparatus happens to be free. Each exercise is to be performed one time only and for the number of repetitions prescribed.

The exercises of the girls' program place emphasis on the hip, thigh, waist, and bust areas although exercises for all the major muscle groups are included. The exercises should be performed in the order listed. However, the beginning exercise may be number 1, alternate curl with dumbbells, for half the class; and exercise number 12, leg push-aways with metal shoes, the beginning exercise for the other half of the class. The order of exercise performance should proceed from that particular exercise on down the list; those starting with exercise number 12 will proceed to exercise number 1 following the performance of exercise number 17. This will provide for a maximum use of equipment with a minimum of waiting.

METHOD OF RESISTANCE INCREASE

The double progressive system of resistance increase is recommended for the exercise programs in Chapter 3. With this system, each exercise scheduled for five repetitions is increased to six at the beginning of the second week, seven at the beginning of the third week, eight at the beginning of the fourth week, and so on up the line until ten repetitions are reached. The weight is then increased a suitable amount (anywhere from $2\frac{1}{2}$ lbs. to 10 lbs., depending upon the exercise and the individual). The repetitions are reduced to five again, and the rate of repetition increase is commenced over again, etc. Those exercises scheduled for ten repetitions are increased by two each week until a total of twenty is reached, and then reduced to ten when the weight is increased, etc.

Best results seem to accrue from a program of progressive weight training when it is conducted on a three-day week (say, Monday, Wednesday, Friday) or on an every other day basis. The weekly increase is applicable to classes conducted on this basis. However, since the two-day week and five-day week programs fit closely to this pattern, the same schedule of repetition increase may be used for them as well.

THE EXERCISE CARD, BASIC PROGRAM. The exercise cards described here were designed for use with a beginning class in progressive weight training. The card has space at the top for the student's name and the date

EASTERN WASHINGTON COLLEGE OF EDUCATION
DIVISION OF HEALTH, PHYSICAL EDUCATION AND RECREATION

PROGRESSIVE WEIGHT TRAINING CARD (BOYS)

NAME ....   DATE.........................

REGULAR EXERCISES	lbs.			REPETITIONS				lbs.			REPETITIONS			
1. Two-Arms Curl		5							5					
2. Press Behind Neck		5							5					
3. Rowing Motion		5							5					
4. Shoulder Shrug		10							10					
5. Straddle Lift		10							10					
6. Rise on Toes		20							20					
7. Reverse Curl		5							5					
8. Side Bend		20							20					
9. Half-Squat		10							10					
10. Two-Arms Press		5							5					
11. Stiff-Legged Dead Lift		10							10					
12. Two-Arms Pull Over		10							10					
13. Sit-Up		10							10					
14. Supine Press		5							5					
15. Wrist Roll		5							5					

SPECIAL EXERCISES   lbs.   reps.   RECORD OF ATTENDANCE

			Month	1	2	3	4	5	6	7	8	9	10	11	12	13	14	15	16	17	18	19	20	21	22	23	24	25	26	27	28	29	30	31
1.			Jan.																															
2.			Feb.																															
3.			Mar.																															
4.			Apr.																															
5.			May																															
			June																															
REMARKS			July																															
			Aug.																															
			Sept.																															
			Oct.																															
			Nov.																															
			Dec.																															

Fig. 4—1. Exercise card, boy's basic program.

he commences his program. The left-hand column beneath the name space contains a list of the exercises to be performed. These are the exercises described in Chapter 3. The first column to the right of the list of exercises contains space for listing the amount of resistance to be used in each exercise. This can be determined roughly from the approximations given in the previous chapter and more accurately after observing the student perform the exercise with the recommended weight. These poundages should be written in pencil so that they may be adjusted when needed. The next group of columns to the right are spaces for recording the number of repetitions that each exercise is to be performed. The first of these should contain the repetitions recommended in the previous chapter. The second is for the recording of the repetitions to be performed the second week, and so on up the line until the maximum of 10 and 20 repetitions is reached as described under "Method of Resistance Increase," above. The next column is for the recording of the new resistance to be used in each exercise and the next repetition column is for the recording of the starting number of repe-

EASTERN WASHINGTON COLLEGE OF EDUCATION
DIVISION OF HEALTH, PHYSICAL EDUCATION AND RECREATION

PROGRESSIVE WEIGHT TRAINING CARD (GIRLS)

NAME_____   DATE_____

REGULAR EXERCISES	lbs.		REPETITIONS				lbs.		REPETITIONS			
1. Alternate Curl		5						5				
2. Alternate Triceps Extension		5						5				
3. Pull-Down to Back of Neck		10						10				
4. Half-Squat		10						10				
5. Rise on Toes		20						20				
6. Front and Lateral Raise		5						5				
7. Inclined Bench Press		5						5				
8. Sit-Up		10						10				
9. Side Bend		20						20				
10. Stiff-Legged Bendover		10						10				
11. Two-Arms Pull-Over		10						10				
12. Leg Push-Aways		10						10				
13. Single-Leg Extension		10						10				
14. Single-Leg Back Extension		10						10				
15. Side-Lying Leg Scissors		10						10				
16. Straight-Legged Bicycle		10						10				
17. Forward Raise on Bench		5						5				

SPECIAL EXERCISES   lbs.   reps.   RECORD OF ATTENDANCE

Month	1	2	3	4	5	6	7	8	9	10	11	12	13	14	15	16	17	18	19	20	21	22	23	24	25	26	27	28	29	30	31
Jan.																															
Feb.																															
Mar.																															
Apr.																															
May																															
June																															
July																															
Aug.																															
Sept.																															
Oct.																															
Nov.																															
Dec.																															

SPECIAL EXERCISES: 1. 2. 3. 4. 5.

REMARKS

Fig. 4—2. Exercise card, girl's basic program.

titions again. The cards are set up for a twelve-weeks period, the approximate length of a college quarter. The card may be used for any period of time by simply extending or reducing the number of lbs. and repetitions columns in accordance with the method of resistance increase. The lower columns on the left are for recording special exercises and any remarks pertinent to the student or his program. The chart at the lower right is for recording attendance or workouts.

Each student should be issued one of these cards which will serve as a guide in recalling the exercise, resistance, repetitions, and sequence as the student progresses through the workout.

It is a good plan to keep these cards in the weight room so that they will not be lost and will be available as a guide should the student desire to perform the exercises at some out-of-class time. For this purpose, the racks illustrated in Fig. 4–3 serve quite adequately. Each student picks up his or her card at the beginning of the period and deposits it in the rack at the close of the period. During the exercise period it is placed in the card holder shown in Fig. 4–4. These are merely sticks, one inch square and

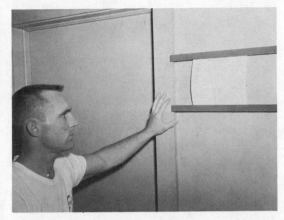

Fig. 4—4.   Exercise card holder.

Fig. 4—3.   Exercise card rack.

grooved to a depth of one-half inch to hold the card. They aid in keeping the cards out of the way and in a position of easy reference during the exercise period.

BASIC INTRODUCTION.   In introducing students to a basic program of progressive weight training, many of the items described in the introduction to this book should be presented. A knowledge of the history of weight training is helpful to the student in understanding the activity. Undoubtedly they have heard some of the fallacious claims concerning it. These should be explained. The student nearly always wants to know "What's in it for me?" He should know what to expect from engaging in the program. Many boys, particularly in junior high or beginning senior high school are interested in strength. Some stories of the old-time strong men are of particular interest to them and are good motivating aids. Strength tests and physical measurements may be taken at this time for use in comparisons and evaluations later on.

EXERCISE PRESENTATION.   There are a number of items that should be stressed on the first class day with the weights, such as the various methods of grasping a weight (the grips), the proper method of lifting a weight or heavy object, the proper method of pushing or pulling a heavy object, the various components of a barbell (bar, plates, and collars), the correct method of computing the weight of the barbell, the correct method of loading and unloading a barbell, the position of the bars on the floor for exercise purposes, the position of the students when not exercising, the use of the exercise card, etc. Most of these items have been dealt with elsewhere in this book and should be explained to the student at the outset of the program.

For the first exercise day, the bars are placed at their places on the floor and loaded to a weight of approximately 30 to 40 pounds. The students should then be paired off according to weight and assigned to a bar. This places the individuals of the closest body weight at the same bar, which will be an aid in that adjusting weights for the exercises is thereby held to a minimum. Although this is not of great benefit for the first few days when the exercises are being demonstrated, it is of considerable benefit during the remainder of the course.

After the students have been assigned to a bar, the instructor explains and demonstrates the various exercises, giving all the particulars listed with the description of each exercise. The students then practice the exercise while the instructor checks for form and answers questions. Initial instruction is speeded up if the instructor explains and demonstrates a few, say three, exercises at a time before having the students attempt them. If too many exercises are explained before a student has a chance to try them, he will become confused. The use of the 30- or 40-pound weight for all exercises during this explanation period also helps hurry this session along. Adjusting weights is not a problem with the girls' program.

EXERCISE SUPERVISION. When all students have completed a practice session with each of the exercises, they should be assisted in determining the correct amount of weight to be used in each exercise. These poundages are recorded on the exercise card, students will use them in performing the different exercises. After the students commence this phase of the program, the roll of the instructor is one of constant supervision to see that the correct amount of resistance and proper form are used throughout the performance of all the exercises. During the first few days, particularly, the amount of resistance has to be altered either up or down to fit each particular student's ability. Remember, the recommended starting resistance is only approximate. Be sure it is considered as just that. Do not hesitate to adjust it where needed. Also, do not hesitate to assist the student with his form. This is quite important. Point out to him where he is performing incorrectly and tell him the method of correcting this and why it should be corrected.

EXERCISE BOARD. A board containing illustrations of the various exercises, such as those in Chapter 3 is helpful. The name of each exercise is written immediately beneath the illustration. Placing such a board on the wall of the room assists in recalling the proper method of performing any particular exercise.

SAFETY FACTORS

1. Keep the weights locked in the racks or the weight room locked except when being used by a class or some other authorized group.

2. Insist that the bars be placed on the floor for loading and unloading. If the plates are removed from one end of a bar only when it is resting on a squat rack or the rack of the multipurpose bench, the bar will catapult to the other side of the rack with a possibility of serious injury or damage being inflicted. Caution students on this possibility.

3. Insist that the collars, both outside and inside, are used on the bars at all times and that they are fastened on securely.

4. Caution students against dropping the bars on end and against dropping barbell plates and dumbbells.

5. Do not permit a student to lift weights unless he is properly attired in gymnasium clothing.

6. Do not permit students to mill around unnecessarily or to engage in any horseplay.

7. Make certain that the student understands and employs the proper method in lifting a weight.

8. Caution the student against using too much weight. It is better to start with a weight that is too light than with one that is too heavy.

9. Instruct the student to respect the positions of the other students when he commences an exercise or lift.

ADVANCED WEIGHT TRAINING PROGRAMS

The basic exercise program lists the exercises in a sequence that permits the exerciser to proceed from one muscle group to the next until all of the major muscle groups of the body have been exercised and then repeats some of the muscle groups with different exercises. Some body builders like to place more emphasis on one set of muscles than another in their workouts, particularly if they feel these groups are sub-par in relation to the other muscle groups of their bodies. Also, there are those advanced body builders striving for physical perfection who desire to exercise one muscle group completely before moving on to the next. They may spend one exercise period on one portion of the body, say arms and chest, and the next exercise period on another portion, say the hips and legs. This type of exercise specialization involves the use of exercise repetitions in units known as sets and requires a considerable amount of time for each workout.

When one exercise is performed for a specified number of repetitions, say the two-arms curl for five repetitions, this is known as one set. If the exercise is repeated for five more repetitions, this is called a second set. If this procedure were included in the exercise program, we would say that the two-arms curl would be performed for two sets of five repetitions each. The number of sets that an exercise may be performed will vary upward from two to five or six sets. Also, the number of repetitions in each set may vary such as becoming less with each set. Added to this, the weight used for each set may vary, usually being increased with each set.

An advanced weight-training program employing the use of sets having the same number of repetitions for each set the exercise is performed is the one used by Harry Johnson in training for the 1959 "Mr. America" contest which he won. His exercises, poundages, sets, and repetitions were as follows: [1]

Exercise	Lbs.	Sets	Repetitions
Bench press	260	3	15
Incline bench press	90 each arm	3	12
Decline press	90 each arm	3	15
Barbell press behind neck	130	3	12
One-arm dumbbell press	85	3	12
Pull-up behind neck	0	3	15
One-arm dumbbell bent-over rowing motion	80	3	15
Barbell curl	135	3	12
One-arm dumbbell concentration curl	55	3	12
Triceps extension while lying on bench	80	3	12
Triceps push-ups	0	3	15
Press from handstand on bench	0	3	12
Hack lift	200	3	15
Toe raise	150	4	20
Abdominal raise on flat board	0	2	500
Leg raise	5 each leg	4	30

A program employing sets of varying poundages and repetitions is used by Roy Hilligenn, "Mr. America" in 1951, in performing the wide grip flat bench press.[2] Five sets are used. The poundages and repetitions employed are as follows: first set, 250 lbs., 10 repetitions; the second set, 260 lbs., 8 repetitions; the third set, 280 lbs., 6 repetitions; the fourth set, 290 lbs., 4 repetitions; and the fifth set, 300 lbs., 2 repetitions.

Programs of these types are for the advanced and serious student of progressive weight training. They require a considerable amount of time. Mr. Johnson's program required approximately two hours to complete, and he performed it three days a week. The beginner should not attempt a program such as this but should first engage in a program similar to the one described in Chapter 3.

The selection of special exercises for the advanced body builder requires the guidance of a person skilled in physical appraisal, as these exercises should fit the needs of the individual. This may be either the body builder

[1] Harry Johnson, "How I Trained for the Mr. America Contest," *Strength and Health*, December 1959, pp. 19-21.

[2] Roy Hilligenn, "High Pecs For 'Low' Bodybuilders," *Mr. America*, Vol. 2, No. 12 (May 1960), pp. 16, 17, 44, 47.

EASTERN WASHINGTON COLLEGE OF EDUCATION
DIVISION OF HEALTH, PHYSICAL EDUCATION AND RECREATION
ADVANCED WEIGHT TRAINING CARD

NAME_____   DATE_____

Exercises	Lbs	Sets	Repetitions
1			
2			
3			
4			
5			
6			
7			
8			
9			
10			
11			
12			
13			
14			
15			
16			
17			
18			
19			
20			

Fig. 4—5.   Exercise card, advanced program.

or his teacher, depending upon the knowledge and experience of both.
Exercises for such a type of program will be listed in Chapter 6. Here,
again, the exercise card is useful; however, it need only contain spaces for
exercises, poundages, sets and repetitions, as shown in Fig. 4–5.

5

Evaluation of the
Exercise Programs

The purposes of a course in progressive weight training are listed in Chapter 1, as well as its justification and place in the educational curriculum. Any course that is a part of the educational curriculum should make positive contributions to the pupils' learning in terms of the acquisition of certain knowledge and fundamental skills. Closely associated with the latter is the development of physical qualities related to good health. Physical size and condition play a part here. Now if knowledge, skills, and physical development are acquired through participation in this course, we should have some means of evaluating these items. In a progressive weight training course, such an evaluation can be made for both boys and girls in each of the three areas. However, the area of skills is not of as much concern in this course as it is in other activity courses in the physical education program.

In the area of physical development there are two aspects that are of primary concern to most students, whether male or female; these are: the increase or decrease in physical measurements, depending upon the wishes of the student; and the improvement in body condition.

MEASUREMENTS OF PHYSICAL SIZE

The measurements of most concern to the boys are: height, weight, neck, upper arm flexed, forearm, chest normal, chest expanded, waist, hips, thigh, and calf.

The measurements of most concern to the girls are: height, weight, neck, upper arm straight, bust, waist, hips, thigh, and calf.

The measurements of the wrist, knee, and ankle will be of interest to both sexes, particularly in terms of development proportions and potential. The age of the individual should also be recorded with the above measurements. All linear measurements, with the exception of height, are circumference measurements. All measurements should be taken at the beginning and at the completion of the progressive weight training course, under the same conditions and, preferably, by the same individual. The measurements should be taken of the student while attired in the regular gymnasium costume, shorts only for boys, and shorts and blouse for girls.

The instruments required for these measurements are: an anthropometer or measuring stick, a steel or linen anthropometric tape, and a beam balance scale. Since most individuals are accustomed to dealing with linear measurements in terms of inches rather than centimeters, it is recommended that these measurements be recorded in inches for clarity.

Age. Record in years and months.

Height
Body position: Erect standing position without shoes, feet together, knees straight, arms at sides, head erect and facing straight ahead, back against anthropometer or wall.

Measurement: Place anthropometer arm, draftsman's triangle or similar object against top of head and wall to determine level. Mark and record height in inches.

Weight
Body position: Erect standing position without shoes, arms at sides.

Measurement: Record in pounds.

In taking girth measurements, the tape should be held at right angles to the long axis of the segment. It should be held in gentle contact with the skin; not loose upon it or compressed into it. Take arm and leg measurements for both sides of the body. Record all girth measurements in inches.

Neck
Body position: Head erect and muscles relaxed.

Measurement: Place tape around smallest part, just above "Adam's Apple."

Upper Arm, Flexed
Body position: Erect standing position, arm held out to side of body at

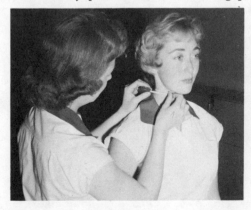

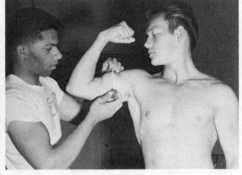

Fig. 5—1. Neck girth measurement.

Fig. 5—2. Upper arm flexed measurement.

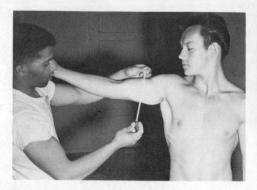

Fig. 5—3. Upper arm straight measurement.

Fig. 5—4. Forearm measurement.

shoulder level, elbow bent, fist clenched with palm toward shoulder, muscles tensed.

Measurement: Place tape around the largest part of the upper arm.

Upper Arm, Straight

Body position: Erect standing position, arm held out to side of body at shoulder level, elbow straight, palm facing up, muscles relaxed.

Measurement: Place tape around the largest part of the upper arm.

Forearm

Body position: Erect standing position as for straight upper arm measurement.

Measurement: Place tape around largest part of the forearm.

Wrist

Body position: Erect standing position, as for straight upper arm measurement.

Measurement: Place tape around the bones at the base of the hand.

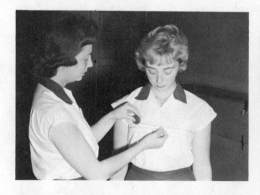

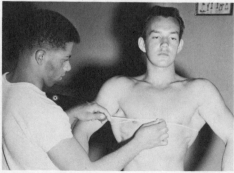

Fig. 5—5. Bust measurement.

Fig. 5—6. Chest expanded measurement.

Chest Normal (Boys); Bust Measurement (Girls)

Body position: Erect standing position with the arms at sides. Breathe normally.

Measurement: Place tape around the chest at nipple height.

Chest Expanded

Body position: Erect standing position; take a deep breath and expand the muscles of the chest and the "lats" (muscles behind the armpits), giving the chest its greatest possible circumference.

Measurement: Place tape around the chest at nipple height.

Waist

Body position: Erect standing position with the arms at sides. Breathe normally, having the abdomen neither drawn in nor protruding.

Measurement: Place tape around the waist at the smallest part, approximately the height of the umbilicus.

Hips

Body position: Erect standing position with the feet together and muscles relaxed.

Measurement: Place tape around largest portion of the hips.

Thigh

Body position: Erect standing position with the feet approximately 18

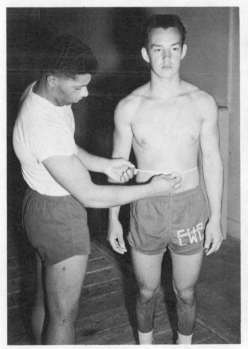

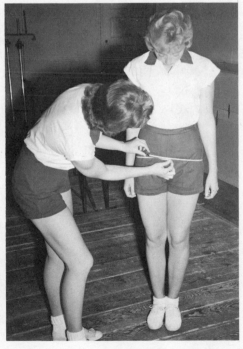

Fig. 5—7.   Waist measurement.   Fig. 5—8.   Hip measurement.

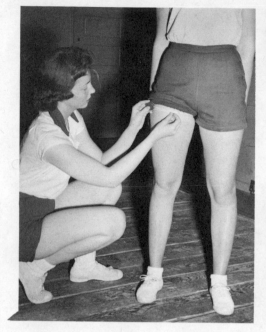 

Fig. 5—9. Thigh measurement.   **Fig. 5—10. Calf measurement.**

inches apart, the weight equally distributed on both feet, and the muscles relaxed.

Measurement: Place tape around the largest part, usually in crease just below buttocks.

Knee

Body position: Erect standing position as for thigh measurement.

Measurement: Place tape around the middle of knee cap.

Calf

Body position: Erect standing position, as for thigh measurement.

Measurement: Place tape around the largest part of the lower leg.

Ankle

Body position: Erect standing position as for thigh measurement.

Measurement: Place tape around smallest part, just above ankle bones.

The male or female body-builder desirous of developing his or her body to the ultimate in terms of symmetry and size will find Willoughby's article "An Anthropometric Method at Arriving at the Optimal Proportions of the Body in Any Adult Individual" of interest.[1]

1 David P. Willoughby, "An Anthropometric Method at Arriving at the Optimal Proportions of the Body in Any Adult Individual," *Research Quarterly*, Vol. 3, No. 1 (March 1932), pp. 48-77.

MEASUREMENTS OF STRENGTH

Since one of the major purposes of a program of progressive weight-training exercises is the development of body strength, some indication of the students' progress toward this goal should be obtained. Any one of a number of strength tests utilizing various types of equipment may be used. However, since many tests of strength require the use of expensive equipment, the following test batteries are suggested.

STRENGTH TEST FOR BOYS. For secondary school boys, the boys' strength test battery of the Washington Association for Health, Physical Education and Recreation is suggested.[2] This test includes the chin, dip, and jump-reach which are indicators of arm, shoulder girdle, and leg strength. These are the items of the Larson Strength Test,[3] but the norms are those established on 8,817 boys from the state of Washington, using a different basis for scoring than that used by Larson.

Chins

Equipment: One chinning bar. Recommended height 7' 11", diameter of bar 1¹⁄₁₆".

Fig. 5—11. Chins.

[2] "Washington State Physical Fitness Test Batteries for Junior-Senior High School Boys and Girls" (Washington Association for Health, Physical Education and Recreation, 1959).

[3] L. A. Larson, "A Factor and Validity Analysis of Strength Variables and Tests With a Combination of Chinning, Dipping and Vertical Jump," *Research Quarterly*, Vol. XI, No. 4 (December 1940), pp. 82-96

Test Description: The subject may use either grip, i.e., palms forward or palms back. (1) The subject jumps and grasps the bar. (2) He bends his elbows and pulls himself up until his chin is above the bar. He then lowers himself to a hang position with the arms completely straight at the elbows, as in (1). This constitutes one chin. He then repeats the movement for as many times as possible.

Caution: Do not allow any kipping or kicking with the legs. Make certain that the subject straightens his arms completely between each chin. If his feet come in contact with the floor, the knees should be bent. Do not permit the subject to drop from the bar during the test.

Score: The number of complete chins that can be performed correctly and consecutively.

Dips

Equipment: One set of dip or parallel bars. Recommended height 5′ 3″, diameter of bar 1½″, width between bars 16½″.

Test Description: (1) The subject jumps or is assisted to an arm support position on the dip or parallel bars. (2) He then lowers himself between the bars until the angle of the arm at the elbow joint is equal to or less than a right angle. The subject then pushes up to extended arm support position, as in (1). This constitutes one dip. He repeats this dipping movement for as many times as possible.

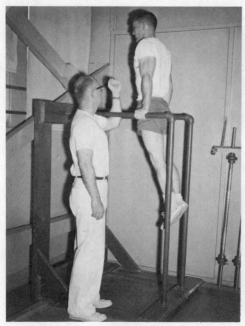

Fig. 5—12.   Dips.

Caution: Do not allow any kipping or kicking with the legs. Make certain that the subject straightens his arms completely at the completion of each dip and that the arms are bent to a right angle during the performance of each dip. To determine the latter more accurately, the tester places his arm against one of the dip bars with his forearm perpendicular to the floor and at such a height that his fist will come in contact with the subjects' shoulder at the time a right angle is reached at the elbow joint. If the subjects' feet come in contact with the floor during the movement, the knees should be bent. Do not permit the subject to drop from the bars during the test.

Score: The number of complete dips that can be performed correctly and consecutively.

Jump-Reach

Equipment: One blackboard 5' x 22" wide fastened to wall, the bottom of which should be 5' 10" from the floor; a piece of chalk; an eraser, a yardstick, and a small ladder or chair for tester.

Test Description: The subject stands facing the wall and as close to it as possible keeping the feet together and flat on the floor. He then reaches upward with both hands as far as possible. (1) A chalk mark is made at the maximum reach at the tips of the fingers for each hand. A line is drawn between these two points. The subject then stands with either side to the wall. Chalk dust is placed on middle finger of hand nearest wall. (2) The subject then bends the knees and ankles, assuming a semi-crouch position with arms swung backward. (3) Then, swinging

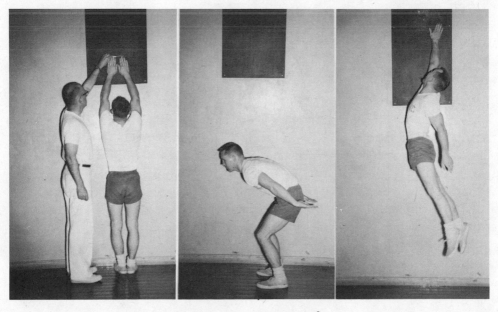

Fig. 5—13. Jump-reach.

the arms forward and upward and extending the legs and ankles, as in a basketball center jump, he jumps as high as possible touching the board at the maximum height of jump.

Caution: In placing the first chalk mark on the wall, make certain that the subject is standing as close to the wall as possible with his feet together and flat on the floor and is reaching upward with both hands as high as possible. Also, the subject is to use the hand nearest the wall for marking the height of the jump, *not* the hand away from the wall. Bounding or double jumps are not permitted.

Score: The test is administered three times, the best mark of the three being recorded. This is the measured distance between the first chalk mark and the highest mark made on the jumps. Record to the nearest half inch.

Strength Scores for Boys.   To determine the strength score for any student, he must be classified according to the McCloy Classification Index.[4] The formula for this is: CI = 20 × age (in years) + 6 × height (in inches) + weight (in pounds). The year value for age over 17 years remains as 17. Thus a boy 17 years of age, 72 inches tall and weighing 150 pounds would have a classification index as follows:

20 × age	=	20 × 17	=	340
6 × height	=	6 × 72	=	432
weight	=		150	=	150
Classification Index	=	Total	=	922

The subjects' class is then determined from the following classification scores:

Class	Score	Class	Score
A	Up to 674	E	780 to 814
B	675 to 709	F	815 to 849
C	710 to 744	G	850 to 884
D	745 to 779	H	885 Up

The subject in the example given above would come under class H since his score in the classification index is 922. His strength score is then determined by referring to the point scores opposite his performance scores in column H in Tables 1–3. The number of points opposite the number of chins, dips, and inches jumped for the classification (H in this case) are added together to give the total strength score (Table 4). Once a class has been determined, it should not be changed during that school year, and all comparisons should be made within this classification.

4 Charles Harold McCloy and Norma Dorothy Young, *Tests and Measurements in Health and Physical Education,* 3d ed. (New York: Appleton-Century-Crofts, Inc., 1954); as reported in "Washington State Physical Fitness Test Batteries for Junor-Senior High School Boys and Girls" (Washington Association for Health, Physical Education and Recreation, 1959).

TABLE 1

POINT SCORES FOR THE CHINS—BOYS' STRENGTH TEST

Class A	Class B	Class C	Class D	Class E	Class F	Class G	Class H	Points
	14-15	17	21	23		20-21		28
16	13		20	22			21	27
15		16	19	21			19-20	26
14		14-15	16-18	19-20	20	19	18	25
13		13	15	16-18	18-19	17-18	17	24
12	11-12	11-12	13-14	14-15	16-17	16	15-16	23
11	9-10	10	11-12	13	14-15	14-15	13-14	22
	8	8-9	10	12	13	12-13	12	21
	6-7	7	8-9	10-11	11-12	11	11	20
8-10	5	6	7	9	10	10	10	19
7	4	4-5	5-6	7-8	8-9	9	8-9	18
4-6	3	3	4	6	7	7-8	7	17
3	2	2	3	5	6	6	6	16
2	1	1	2	4	4-5	4-5	4-5	15
			1	2-3	3	3	3	14
1				1	2	2	2	13
					1	1		12
								11
							1	10

TABLE 2

POINT SCORES FOR THE DIPS—BOYS' STRENGTH TEST

Class A	Class B	Class C	Class D	Class E	Class F	Class G	Class H	Points
			32-33	29-30		37-38		28
20	31	20	31	27-28		33-36	28-30	27
18-19	22-30	17-19	21-30	23-26	24-27	25-32	23-27	26
16-17	16-21	15-16	18-20	20-22	21-23	21-24	20-22	25
14-15	14-15	14	16-17	17-19	20	18-20	18-19	24
11-13	12-13	12-13	14-15	15-16	17-19	16-17	17	23
	9-11	9-11	12-13	13-14	15-16	14-15	15-16	22
	8	8	10-11	12	13-14	13	14	21
10	6-7	6-7	7-9	9-11	11-12	11-12	11-13	20
7-9	4-5	4-5		7-8	9-10	9-10	10	19
5-6	3	3	5-6	6	8	8	8-9	18
3-4	2	2	3-4	4-5	6-7	6-7	6-7	17
2	1	1	2	3	4-5	5	5	16
			1	1-2	3	3-4	3-4	15
1					1-2	2	2	14
						1	1	13

TABLE 3

POINT SCORES FOR THE JUMP-REACH—BOYS' STRENGTH TEST

Class A	Class B	Class C	Class D	Class E	Class F	Class G	Class H	Points
22								29
		23	24½	27 -28½	32 -36	31½		28
20½-21½	21½-22	22½	23½-24	25½-26½	27½-31½	30 -31		27
20	21	21½-22	23	25	26½-27	27 -29½	27	26
19 -19½	20½	20½-21	21½-22½	23½-24½	25 -26	25½-26½	26 -26½	25
18 -18½	19 -20	19½-20	21	22½-23	23½-24½	24½-25	25 -25½	24
17 -17½	17 -18½	18½-19	20 -20½	21½-22	22½-23	23½-24	24 -24½	23
16 -16½	16½	17½-18	19 -19½	20½-21	22	23	23 -23½	22
15½	15½-16	17	18½	19½-20	21 -21½	22 -22½	22½	21
14½-15		16 -16½	17½-18	18½-19	20 -20½	21 -21½	21½-22	20
14	15	15½	16½-17	17½-18	19 -19½	20 -20½	20½-21	19
13 -13½	14 -14½	14½-15	15½-16	16½-17	18 -18½	19 -19½	19½-20	18
12½	13 -13½	13½-14	14½-15	16	17½	18 -18½	18½-19	17
12	12½	13	13½-14	15 -15½	16½-17	17 -17½	17½-18	16
11½	11½-12	12 -12½	13	14 -14½	15½-16	16 -16½	16½-17	15
10½-11	11	11 -11½	11½-12½	12½-13½	14 -15	14½-15½	15½-16	14
10	10 -10½	10 -10½	10½-11	11½-12	12½-13½	13½-14	14 -15	13
9½	9½	9½	9½-10	9½-11	11 -12	12½-13	13 -13½	12
	8 - 9	8 - 9	8½- 9	8½-9	9½-10½	10½-12	12½	11
9	7½	7½	8	8	8½- 9		10 -12	10
	7	7	7½		8		9 - 9½	9
8½	6½	5 - 6½	7	7½	6 - 7½	10	8½	8
7½- 8		4½	4½- 6½	7	5½	9 - 9½		7
		4		6½	4 - 5	8½		6
	6						8	5
6 - 7			4			8		4
						7½		3

TABLE 4

NORMS FOR TOTAL STRENGTH—BOYS

Class A	Class B	Class C	Class D	Class E	Class F	Class G	Class H	Rating
67-up	69-up	69-up	68-up	69-up	68-up	69-up	67-up	Superior
54-66	53-68	56-68	54-67	58-68	57-67	57-68	57-66	Good
48-53	43-52	49-55	47-53	46-57	46-56	45-56	45-56	Average
37-47	32-42	42-48	40-46	39-45	37-45	36-44	33-44	Poor
36-down	31-down	41-down	39-down	38-down	36-down	35-down	32-down	Very Poor

STRENGTH TEST FOR GIRLS. The Washington Association for Health, Physical Education and Recreation strength test battery for girls is suggested here. This test includes the pull-up, sit-up and jump-reach which are indicators of arm and shoulder, abdominal and leg strength. The norms for this battery of strength tests were established on 3,494 girls from the state of Washington.

Fig. 5—14.   Pull-ups.

Pull-ups

Equipment: One wand, with a ribbon attached which hangs six inches long, for every three students.

Test Description: The subject lies flat on her back on the floor. Two students stand on either side in a forward lunge position, one facing in the direction of the subjects' feet, the other in the direction of her head. They hold the wand so that it is supported by their forward thighs at the point directly above the subject's shoulders at the height of full reach. The wand is so held that the students holding it can just see the top of the ribbon as the ribbon hangs straight down. (1) The subject grasps the wand with her hands using either grip, i.e. palms forward or palms back. (2) Keeping a straight line from heels to head, the subject pulls upward until her chest touches the ribbon (i.e., the ribbon moves); then returns to a reclining position, as in (1). This constitutes one pull-up. She repeats the movement for as many times as possible. The students rotate doing the pull-ups until all have taken the test.

Caution: Make certain that the subject being tested keeps her body in a straight line, touches the ribbon with her chest, and returns to a reclining position on the floor between each pull-up. Also, make certain that the students holding the wand understand that they are not to assist the subject in any manner.

Score: The number of complete pull-ups that can be done correctly and consecutively.

Sit-ups

Equipment: None.

Test Description: (1) The subject lies on her back with head and shoulders touching the floor, arms crossed in front of body, hands over shoul-

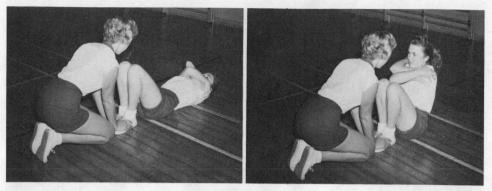

Fig. 5—15. Sit-ups.

ders, knees bent so that the feet are flat on the floor with the heels close
to the seat. (2) With the feet held flat by her partner, she comes to a
sitting position touching her elbows to her knees, and then returns to
starting position, as in (1). This constitutes one sit-up. She repeats this
movement for as many times as possible up to fifty.

Caution: The subjects' feet must be kept flat on the floor and close to
the seat. The head and shoulders must touch the floor each time. The
elbows must touch the knees.

Score: The number of complete sit-ups up to fifty that can be done correctly and consecutively.

Jump-Reach. The jump-reach test for girls is identical to that administered to boys in equipment, method of performing the test, and scoring.
See page 73 for this test.

Fig. 5—16. Jump-reach.

Strength Scores for Girls. To determine the strength score for a girl, refer to the point scores (in Tables 5–7) opposite her performance scores that correspond with the student's grade level in school. The number of points opposite the number of pull-ups, sit-ups, and inches jumped for her grade level are added together to give the total strength score (Table 8). All comparisons should be made within this grade level.

TABLE 5
POINT SCORES FOR THE PULL-UPS—GIRLS' STRENGTH TEST

Grade 7	Grade 8	Grade 9	Grade 10	Grade 11	Grade 12	Points
36						28
34-35	32-40	38-40	26-30	30		27
32-33	30-31	32-37	25	27-29		26
30-31	27-29	30-31	23-24	26		25
26-29	24-26	26-29	21-22	23-25	22-23	24
22-25	21-23	23-25	19-20	21-22	20-21	23
20-21	19-20	21-22	16-18	19-20	15-19	22
17-19	16-18	19-20	14-15	15-18	13-14	21
15-16	14-15	16-18	13	13-14	11-12	20
13-14	12-13	14-15	11-12	11-12	9-10	19
12	10-11	12-13	10	10	8	18
10-11	9	11	9	8-9	7	17
8-9	7-8	9-10	7-8	7	6	16
7	6	8	5-6	6	5	15
6	5	7	4	5	4	14
4-5	4	5-6	3	3-4	3	13
3	2-3	4	2	2	1-2	12
2	1	2-3	1	1		11
1		1				10

TABLE 6
POINT SCORES FOR THE SIT-UPS—GIRLS' STRENGTH TEST

Grade 7	Grade 8	Grade 9	Grade 10	Grade 11	Grade 12	Points
					50	24
			50	50	46-49	23
50	50		44-49	45-49	41-45	22
		50	36-43	37-44	31-40	21
37-49	40-49	42-49	31-35	31-36	27-30	20
31-36	33-39	34-41	28-30	27-30	25-26	19
27-30	29-32	30-33	23-27	21-26	20-24	18
23-26	25-28	25-29	20-22	18-20	16-19	17
20-22	21-24	21-24	16-19	15-17	14-15	16
17-19	19-20	18-20	13-15	12-14	11-13	15
14-16	15-18	15-17	10-12	9-11	8-10	14
12-13	13-14	12-14	8-9	6-8	5-7	13
9-11	10-12	10-11	5-7	3-5	1-4	12
8	8-9	8-9	3-4	2		11
5-7	5-7	5-7	1-2	1		10
2-4		3-4				9
1		2				8
						7
		1				6

TABLE 7

Point Scores for the Jump-Reach—Girls' Strength Test

Grade 7	Grade 8	Grade 9	Grade 10	Grade 11	Grade 12	Points
			20½			28
20				22½		27
19 -19½	18½		20	22		26
17 -18½	18	18½-19	19½	19½-21½	22	25
16 -16½	16½-17½	18	18½-19	19	20 -21½	24
15 -15½	16	16½-17½	17½-18	18 -18½	18½-19½	23
14 -14½	15 -15½	16	16½-17	17 -17½	16 -18	22
13½	14½	15½	15½-16	15½-16½	15½	21
12½-13	13 -14	14 -14½	14½-15	14½-15	14½-15	20
12	12½	13½	14	13½-14	14	19
11½	12	12½-13	13½	13	13 -13½	18
10½-11	11½	12	12 -12½	12 -12½	12½	17
10	10½-11	11 -11½	11½	11½	12	16
9 - 9½	10	10½	10½-11	10½-11	11½	15
8½	9½	9½-10	10	10	11	14
8	9	9	9 - 9½.	9 - 9½	10 -10½	13
7½	8 - 8½	8 - 8½	8½	8½	9½	12
7	7 - 7½	7 - 7½	8	8	9	11
6½	6½	6 - 6½	7 - 7½	7½	8 - 8½	10
6	5½- 6	5 - 5½	6½	7	7½	9
4½- 5½	4 - 5	4½	6	6½		8
½- 4	3½	4	4½- 5½			7
			3½			6

TABLE 8

Norms for Total Strength—Girls

Grade 7	Grade 8	Grade 9	Grade 10	Grade 11	Grade 12	Rating
67-up	68-up	66-up	70-up	69-up	71-up	Superior
56-66	57-67	55-65	58-69	58-68	61-70	Good
44-55	44-56	43-54	46-57	46-57	48-60	Average
32-43	35-43	33-42	35-45	36-45	36-47	Poor
31-down	34-down	32-down	34-down	35-down	35-down	Very Poor

TESTS OF ACQUIRED KNOWLEDGE

As has been noted, the knowledge a person gains of the construction and functioning of his body, of the purposes of weight training, and of the activity itself, are important outcomes of this course. Some of this knowledge can be determined through a written examination administered at the completion of the course or unit. Such an examination might include the following questions:

1. (a) List the various exercises you have followed.
   (b) List the muscle or muscles each exercise was designed to develop.

    (c) List the number of starting repetitions recommended for each exercise.

    (d) List the recommended approximate starting resistance for each exercise. (To aid in test correction, this question may be written in four adjoining columns.)

2. Describe completely the method of performing (a) the sit-up exercise and (b) the two-arms pullover exercise.

3. Describe the proper method of breathing during exercise performance.

4. What is the reason for the emphasis placed on proper form in the performance of each exercise?

5. What was the contribution of Alan Calvert to the development of progressive weight training?

6. Are the terms weight lifting and progressive weight training synonyms for the same activity? Explain your answer.

7. Describe the proper method of lifting a weight from the floor.

PHYSICAL SKILL EVALUATION

A majority of the skills in progressive weight training are those of gross body movements, such as elbow flexion and extension in the performance of the two-arms curl, hip and knee flexion and extension in the performance of the half-squat, etc. For most students these will not be skills that will need perfecting as they will already have developed a certain degree of skill in them. However, for the student whose motor coordination is below average, or one who has had little experience with physical activity, these skills may require some effort to master. In such instances the development of these skills can be rated as real progress. These skills along with the skill of moving a weight are usually the only ones of concern in the girls' program.

In addition to the foregoing, the boys' or men's program may include practice in the performance of the three Olympic lifts—the press, the snatch, and the clean and jerk (described in Chapter 7). Although the total amount of weight lifted is the ultimate goal in the practice of these lifts, the form with which each lift is executed may be rated much in the same manner as skill in tumbling or gymnastics is rated; say, on a basis of zero to ten points, depending upon the amount of skill shown in each of the three lifts. The total of these ratings would be the score obtained. This same technique could be applied to the basic movements, if the instructor wished an evaluation here.

COURSE GRADING

Several possibilities have been presented with which a course in progressive weight training may be evaluated: measurements of physical size, measurements of strength, tests for acquired knowledge, and physical skill evaluation. These also serve as positive motivators to the students.

By recording the measurements of physical size and strength at the beginning and again at the completion of the course, changes in these measurements may be noted and rated. Although these will vary with each individual, they will be more stable than a person might originally be led to believe. The use of any or all of these means of evaluation, as well as any other that the person teaching the course may feel is important, is, of course, up to the instructor.

6

Special Exercises
and Specialization

Two recommended exercise programs for beginners, whether boys and girls in a school or men or women in a home or studio situation, have been presented in Chapter 3. The exercises in this chapter are for those who have completed this program and desire to go in for more advanced work or who, for one reason or another (such as athletic participation), desire to specialize in certain areas of the body. A person should not engage in a program of specialization until he has conditioned his body, preferably through the appropriate basic program of Chapter 3. It is also recommended that if only one course in progressive weight training is offered in the school program, it be these basic programs and not one involving specialization.

The exercises comprising the basic boys' or girls' programs are designed to develop the major areas of the body symmetrically. Most individuals new to the program need this emphasis. Specialization does not provide this. Added to this is the factor that special exercises should be prescribed only by an individual who is thoroughly familiar with the field and with the anatomy, physiology, and mechanics of the body. However, for those individuals who are ready for advanced work and for those who are qualified to administer these advanced and specialized programs, this chapter is presented.

USE OF SETS. As explained in Chapter 4, a set is the performance of one exercise for a specified number of repetitions once. Two sets, then, would be the performance of one exercise for a specified number of repetitions twice. Three sets would be the performance of this exercise for a specified number of repetitions three times. This places a concentration of work on a specific group of muscles before moving to another group. It differs from the basic programs in Chapter 3 where the exercises are not performed with this degree of concentration and where the progression moves with each succeeding exercise to a different muscle group of the body.

Since individuals differ from one another in their physical characteristics, it is reasonable to expect them to differ in the type of exercise program that will give them maximum results. From information based on a question-naire study by McQueen of seventeen finalists in the 1953 "Mr. Britain" physique contest,[1] it would seem that the ultimate in muscular develop-ment is most likely to result from the programs employing the maximum poundage that can be lifted in each exercise for the stated number of repeti-tions of each set, and increasing resistance each week in terms of added poundage. The exercise programs were changed each six to eight weeks to prevent the development of staleness and boredom and to assure continued progression. The subjects in this study, however, varied as to the number of sets (3–7) and number of repetitions (9–16) used per exercise. McQueen's study also indicated that weight lifters, training for lifting competition, preferred programs employing sets of decreasing repetitions and increasing poundages. The advanced body builder and lifter will have to resort to some experimentation to determine the program best suited to himself. For most individuals, however, the writer recommends the use of three sets of equal repetitions, these repetitions being the number suggested in each exercise description. The use of sets is not recommended in the women's program.

SPECIAL EXERCISES.* For ease of selection, the exercises in this chapter have been grouped under the general body areas they most specifically affect. Some may be found listed under more than one area as they con-tribute to the development of the muscles in both or all of these areas. Many of the exercises are those already described under previous programs. These will be listed but the reader will need to refer back for the exercise description. The exercises should be selected and a program developed to fit the specific needs of the individual concerned.

FOR THE ARM AND SHOULDER

1. TWO-ARMS CURL WITH BARBELL
Exercise: Refer to page 28 for the description.

2. REVERSE CURL WITH BARBELL
Exercise: Refer to page 33 for the description.

*3. ALTERNATE CURL WITH DUMBBELLS
Exercise: Refer to page 41 for the description. For men, *resistance:* 10-30 lbs.; *starting repetitions:* 10.

---

[1] I. J. McQueen, "Recent Advances in the Technique of Progressive Resistance Exercise," *British Medical Journal*, Vol. 2 (1954), p. 328, as reported in Sidney Licht (ed.), *Therapeutic Exercise* (New Haven: Elizabeth Licht, Publisher, 1958), pp. 293-94.

* Those exercises recommended for women as well as for men are starred.

Fig. 6—1. One-arm curl with dumbbell.

*4. ONE-ARM CURL WITH DUMBBELL

Starting position: Erect standing position with arms at sides, one hand grasping a dumbbell with the palm facing forward.

Movement: (1) Bend the arm at the elbow and bring the dumbbell to the shoulder. (2) Return to starting position.

Resistance: For men, 10-30 lbs.; for women, 3-10 lbs.

Starting repetitions: For men, 10; for women, 5; each arm.

Cadence: Slow.

Caution: Do not bend backward at the waist or move elbow backward from the sides of the body.

Principal muscles affected: Biceps and brachialis of the front of the upper arm.

5. ONE-ARM CONCENTRATION CURL WITH DUMBBELL

Starting position: Seated position on bench with knees spread apart, one elbow resting on the knee of the corresponding leg, the other arm extended downward, elbow resting against inside of knee of same side of body, hand grasping dumbbell, palm forward.

Movement: (1) Bend the arm at the elbow and bring the dumbbell to the shoulder. (2) Return to starting position.

Fig. 6—2.   One-arm concentration curl with dumbbell.

Resistance: 10-30 lbs.

Starting repetitions: 10, each arm.

Cadence: Slow.

Caution: See that the arm is completely extended during the performance of each repetition. The elbow should be supported against the inside of the leg throughout the movement.

Principal muscles affected: Biceps and brachialis of the front of the upper arm.

6. TWO-ARMS CHIN, USING CHINNING BAR

Starting position: Hanging position, arms completely extended, hands

Fig. 6—3.   Two-arms chin, using chinning bar.

grasping bar with under-grip (palms facing back) approximately shoulder-width apart.

Movement: (1) Flex the arms at the elbows bringing the chin to a position just above the bar. (2) Return to starting position.

Resistance: 0. Resistance may be added by attaching barbell plates or a dumbbell to the front of the body by means of a belt around the waist.

Starting repetitions: 5.

Cadence: Moderate.

Caution: Do not allow any kipping or kicking with the legs. Make certain that the arms are completely straightened between each chin. If the feet come in contact with the floor, the knees should be bent.

Principal muscles affected: Biceps and brachialis of the front of the upper arm and the latissimus dorsi of the back.

7. PULL-DOWN TO CHEST, USING LAT MACHINE

Starting position: Sitting position astride bench directly beneath bar of lat machine. Arms extended overhead, hands grasping bar with under-grip (palms facing back) approximately shoulder-width apart.

Movement: (1) Pull bar down to chest. (2) Return to starting position.

Resistance: 50-100 lbs. In calculating this resistance, the weight of the lat machine bar (aproximately 15 lbs.) must be subtracted from the amount of weight on the loading bar to give the actual amount of resistance. The reason for this is that the bar is attached to the cable on the opposing side to the weights and hence provides a 15-lbs. assist in rais-

Fig. 6—4. Pull-down to chest, using lat machine.

ing the weight. Thus to provide 50-lbs. resistance on the lat machine, one must place approximately 65 lbs. of weight on the loading bar.

Starting repetitions: 10.

Cadence: Moderate.

Caution: Keep feet out of the way of the descending weights and sit sufficiently beneath the outer pulley of the lat machine in order to maintain an erect back position.

Principal muscles affected: Biceps and brachialis of the upper arm and the latissimus dorsi of the back.

8. PULL-UP TO BACK OF NECK, USING CHINNING BAR

Starting position: Hanging position, arms completely extended, hands grasping bar with over-grip (palms facing forward) considerably greater than shoulder-width apart.

Movement: (1) Flex the arms at the elbows bringing the back of the neck to the height of the bar. (2) Return to starting position.

Resistance: 0. Resistance may be added by attaching barbell plates or a dumbbell to the front of the body by means of a belt around the waist.

Starting repetitions: 5.

Cadence: Moderate.

Caution: Do not allow any kipping or kicking with the legs. Make certain that the arms are completely straightened between each pull-up. If the feet come in contact with the floor, the knees should be bent.

Principal muscles affected: Biceps and brachialis of the front of the upper arm, latissimus dorsi of the back, and teres major and minor, and trapezius of the upper back.

Fig. 6—5. Pull-up to back of neck, using chinning bar.

*9. PULL-DOWN TO BACK OF NECK, USING LAT MACHINE

Exercise: Refer to page 43 for the description. For men, *resistance:* 50-100 lbs.

10. TWO-ARMS PRESS WITH BARBELL

Exercise: Refer to page 35 for the description.

11. PRESS BEHIND NECK WITH BARBELL

Exercise: Refer to page 28 for the description.

*12. ALTERNATE PRESS WITH DUMBBELLS

Starting position: Erect standing position, hands grasping dumbbells at shoulder level, feet comfortably apart.

Movement: Extend the right arm overhead, then lower it to the starting position. As the dumbbell in the right arm is being lowered, extend the left arm pushing the left dumbbell to arm's length overhead. Keep the arms moving alternately until the prescribed number of repetitions is completed.

Resistance: For men, 10-40 lbs.; for women, 3-10 lbs., each arm.

Starting repetitions: For men, 10; for women, 5. A complete press movement by both arms constitutes one repetition.

Cadence: Moderate.

Fig. 6—6. Alternate press with dumbbells.

Caution: The erect standing position should be maintained and the arms completely extended and the dumbbells returned to the shoulders in the performance of each exercise repetition.

Principal muscles affected: Triceps of the back of the upper arm and deltoid of the shoulder.

*13. ONE-ARM PRESS WITH DUMBBELL

Fig. 6—7. One-arm press with dumbbell.

Starting position: Erect standing position, feet comfortably apart, one hand grasping a dumbbell at shoulder level, the other arm extended sideward at shoulder level.

Movement: (1) Extend the arm, pushing the dumbbell to arm's length overhead. (2) Return to starting position.

Resistance: For men, 10-40 lbs.; for women, 3-10 lbs.

Starting repetitions: For men, 10; for women, 5; each arm.

Cadence: Slow.

Caution: The erect standing position should be maintained and the arm completely extended and the dumbbell returned to the shoulder in the performance of each exercise repetition.

Principal muscles affected: Triceps of the back of the upper arm and deltoid of the shoulder.

*14. INCLINED-BENCH PRESS WITH DUMBBELLS

Exercise: Refer to page 47 for the description. For men, *resistance:* 10-40 lbs. each arm; *starting repetitions:* 10.

15. DECLINED-BENCH PRESS WITH DUMBBELLS

Starting position: Reclining position, back against declined bench, feet held by strap at raised end, head and shoulders at lower end, dumbbells held at shoulder height and a short distance away from the body.

Movement: (1) Extend the arms upward above the chest until the arms are straight and the dumbbells close together. (2) Return to starting position.

Resistance: 10-40 lbs., each arm.

Starting repetitions: 10.

Cadence: Slow.

Caution: The arms should move the dumbbells directly upward over the chest. The elbows should be stretched backward at the shoulders during count 2.

Principal muscles affected: Pectoralis major of the chest, triceps of the back of the upper arm, and deltoid of the shoulder.

Fig. 6—8. Declined bench press with dumbbells.

16. SUPINE PRESS WITH BARBELL

Exercise: Refer to page 38 for the description.

17. TRICEPS EXTENSION WITH BARBELL

Starting position: Lying position with back on bench and arms extended upward, hands grasping bar with the under-grip, approximately shoulder-width apart.

Movement: (1) Bend the arms at the elbows bringing the bar to a position near the top of the head. (2) Extend the arms at the elbows, returning the bar to the starting position.

Resistance: 25-50 lbs.

Starting repetitions: 10.

Fig. 6—9. Triceps extension with barbell.

Cadence: Slow.

Caution: There should be minimal movement of the upper arms. The principal movement should be by the forearms at the elbow joints.

Principal muscles affected: Triceps of the back of the upper arm.

18. FRENCH PRESS WITH DUMBBELL

Fig. 6—10. French press with dumbbell.

Starting position: Erect standing position with feet comfortably apart or sitting position on bench, arms extended overhead, both hands grasping dumbbell by one of the globe ends.

Movement: (1) Bend the arms at the elbows, lowering the dumbbell down the back. (2) Extend the arms at the elbows, returning the dumbbell to the starting position.

Resistance: 20-50 lbs.

Starting repetitions: 10.

Cadence: Slow.

Caution: There should be minimal movement of the upper arms. The principal movement should be by the forearms at the elbow joints.

Principal muscles affected: Triceps of the back of the upper arm.

Substitution: A barbell may be substituted for the dumbbell in the performance of this exercise. If this is done, the bar should be grasped with the over-grip, hands close together.

19. TRICEPS EXTENSION, USING LAT MACHINE

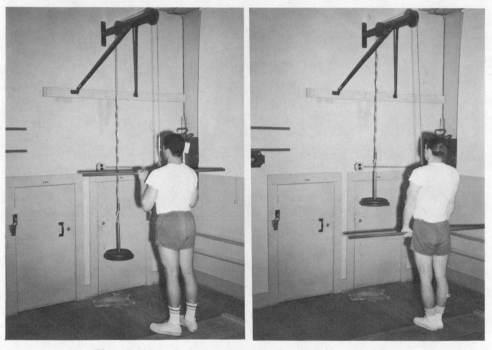

Fig. 6—11. Triceps extension, using lat machine.

Starting position: Erect standing position, arms extended downward in front of the body, hands grasping bar with the over-grip, approximately shoulder-width apart.

Movement: (1) Bend the arms at the elbows bringing the bar to a position in front of the chest. (2) Extend the arms at the elbows, returning the bar to starting position.

Resistance: 25-50 lbs.

Starting repetitions: 10.

Cadence: Slow.

Caution: There should be minimal movement of the upper arms. The principal movement should be by the forearms at the elbow joints.

Principal muscles affected: Triceps of the back of the upper arm.

*20. ALTERNATE TRICEPS EXTENSION WITH DUMBBELLS

Exercise: Refer to page 42 for the description. For men, *resistance:* 10-30 lbs., each arm; *starting repetitions:* 10.

*21. ONE-ARM TRICEPS EXTENSION WITH DUMBBELL

Starting position: Lying position with back on floor or bench, one arm extended upward grasping dumbbell, the other hand supporting elbow of dumbbell arm.

Fig. 6—12.   One-arm triceps extension with dumbbell.

Movement: (1) Bend the arm at the elbow and bring the dumbbell to the shoulder. (2) Extend the forearm at the elbow joint, returning the dumbbell to starting position.

Resistance: For men, 10-40 lbs.; for women, 3-10 lbs.

Starting repetitions: For men, 10; for women, 5; for each arm.

Cadence: Slow.

Caution: There should be no movement of the upper arm, which the supporting hand should aid in preventing. All movement should be by the forearm at the elbow joint.

Principal muscles affected: Triceps of the back of the upper arm.

22. TRICEPS EXTENSION FROM INCLINED POSITION WITH DUMBBELLS

Starting position: Standing position, feet comfortably apart, body inclined forward 90 degrees at the hips, upper arms at sides of body, fore-

Fig. 6—13. Triceps extension from inclined position with dumbbells.

arms inclined downward 90 degrees at elbows, hands grasping dumbbells, knuckles out.

Movement: (1) Straighten the arms at the elbow joint, moving the forearms upward in line with the upper arms. (2) Return to starting position.

Resistance: 10-30 lbs. for each arm.

Starting repetitions: 10.

Cadence: Slow.

Caution: The upper back should remain flat. Bend the knees if necessary. All movement should take place at the elbow joint, the upper arms remaining stationary. The arms should be completely extended during count (1) of the movement.

Principal muscles affected: Triceps of the back of the upper arm.

23. TRICEPS PUSH-UP, USING BENCH

Starting position: Inclined back leaning rest position with feet together,

Fig. 6—14. Triceps push-up, using bench.

heels resting on floor, arms straight with hands grasping end of bench, approximately shoulder-width apart.

Movement: (1) Bend the body at the hips and the arms at the elbows, lowering the seat to the floor. (2) Push up to starting position.

Resistance: 0. Feet may be placed on second bench and barbell plate attached to waist for added resistance.

Starting repetitions: 10.

Cadence: Moderate.

Caution: Straighten body and extend arms completely during count 2.

Principal muscles affected: Triceps of the back of the upper arm.

24. REGULAR PUSH-UP, USING BENCHES

Fig. 6—15. Regular push-up, using benches.

Starting position: Supported front leaning rest position with feet together and on one bench, the arms extended downward, each hand supported on a separate bench, a little more than shoulder-width apart.

Movement: (1) Bend the arms at the elbows, lowering the body between the two benches supporting the hands. (2) Push up to starting position.

Resistance: 0. Resistance may be added by placing a barbell plate on the upper back at the position of the shoulder blades.

Starting repetitions: 10.

Cadence: Moderate.

Caution: Keep the body straight throughout the movement.

Principal muscles affected: Triceps of the back of the upper arm, pectoralis major of the front of the chest, and deltoid of the shoulder.

25. DIPS, USING PARALLEL OR DIP BARS

Starting position: Erect arm-support position on the bars, arms straight, legs together, and feet suspended above the floor.

Movement: (1) Bend the arms at the elbows and lower the shoulders toward the parallel or dip bars and the body between the bars. (2) Push up to starting position.

Resistance: 0. Resistance may be added by attaching barbell plates or a dumbbell to the front of the body by means of a belt around the waist.

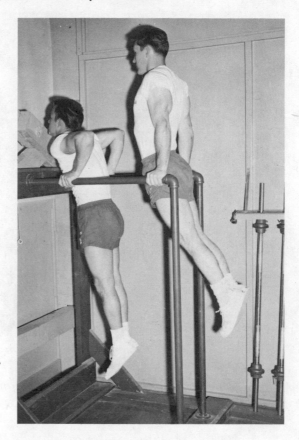

Fig. 6—16. Dips, using dip bars.

Starting repetitions: 5.

Cadence: Moderate.

Caution: There should be no kipping or kicking with the legs. The arms should be straightened completely at the finish of each dip.

Principal muscles affected: Triceps of the back of the upper arm, latissimus dorsi of the back, and trapezius and rhomboid major and minor of the upper back.

26. WRIST ROLL, USING WRIST-ROLL MACHINE OR STICK AND ROPE

Exercise: Refer to page 39 for the description.

27. WRIST CURL WITH BARBELL

Exercise: Refer to page 40 for the description.

28. REVERSE WRIST CURL WITH BARBELL

Exercise: Refer to page 41 for the description.

29. LATERAL WRIST CURL WITH SHORT BAR AND WEIGHT

Starting position: Erect standing position, feet comfortably apart, arms at sides of body, one hand grasping end of short bar extending beyond the thumb side of the hand with barbell plate attached to far end, the thumb side of hand being in extended position.

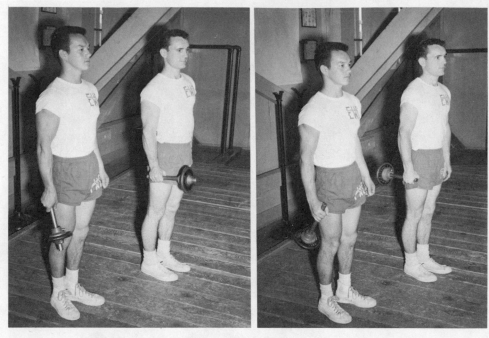

Fig. 6—17.   Lateral wrist curl with short bar and weight.

Movement: (1) Laterally flex the thumb side of hand. (2) Return to starting position.

Resistance: 2½-10 lbs.

Starting repetitions: 5 for each hand. The bar should then be extended from the little-finger side of the hand and the same movement performed.

Cadence: Slow.

Caution: All movement should be at the wrist joint.

Principal muscles affected: Flexor (flexor carpi radialis, flexor carpi ulnaris, flexor pollicus longus) and extensor (extensor carpi radialis longus, extensor carpi radialis brevis, abductor pollicus longus, etc.) muscles of the forearm.

30. ALTERNATE GRASPING, USING BARBELL PLATE

Starting position: Sitting position on bench, feet spread apart, arms extended downward between the legs, one hand grasping a barbell plate by the edge with fingers extended downward.

Movement: Release barbell plate with one hand and grasp it with the other, alternating hands.

Resistance: 10-25 lbs.

Starting repetitions: 5 each hand.

Cadence: Moderate.

Caution: Feet should be outside of barbell plate area. Lift plate slightly upward just before it is released and regrasped.

Fig. 6—18. Alternate grasping, using barbell plate.

Principal muscles affected: Flexor muscles of the forearm and hand (flexor pollicus brevis, adductor pollicus, etc.).

*31. FRONT AND LATERAL RAISE WITH DUMBBELLS

Exercise: Refer to page 46 for the description. For men, *resistance:* 10-25 lbs., cach arm.

*32. LATERAL INCLINED-BENCH RAISE WITH DUMBBELL

Starting position: Standing position with one arm and side against a nearly erect inclined bench, opposite arm at side, hand grasping dumbbell, knuckles away from body.

Fig. 6—19. Lateral inclined-bench raise with dumbbell.

Movement: (1) Raise the arm laterally away from the body until it reaches shoulder level. (2) Return to starting position.

Resistance: For men, 10-25 lbs.; for women, 3-5 lbs.

Starting repetitions: For men, 10; for women, 5, for each arm.

Cadence: Slow.

Caution: Move the arm directly sideward at the shoulder with knuckles up.

Principal muscles affected: Deltoid muscles of the shoulder and trapezius of the upper back.

FOR THE NECK

33. SHOULDER SHRUG WITH BARBELL

Exercise: Refer to page 30 for the description.

34. NECK CURL WITH HEADSTRAP AND WEIGHT

Starting position: Lying position with back on bench, hands grasping headstrap, head and neck projecting beyond bench end, headstrap fastened to head, head extended downward.

Movement: (1) Raise head upward and forward as far as possible. (2) Return to starting position.

Resistance: 5-15 lbs.

Starting repetitions: 5.

Cadence: Slow.

Caution: Be sure that headstrap is adequately secured to prevent slipping from head.

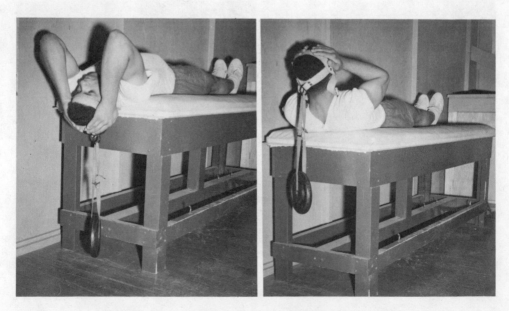

Fig. 6—20.   Neck curl with headstrap and weight.

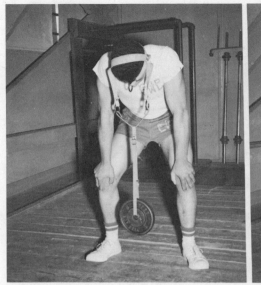 

Fig. 6—21.   Neck extension with headstrap and weight.

Principal muscles affected: Sternocleidomastoid, longus capitus, longus colli, etc., muscles of the front of the neck.

35. NECK EXTENSION WITH HEADSTRAP AND WEIGHT

Starting position: Standing position, feet comfortably apart, back straight, hips and knees flexed, arms straight with hands grasping knees, headstrap fastened to head with weight hanging in front of body, head flexed downward.

Movement: (1) Extend neck, bringing head upward and backward as far as possible. (2) Return to starting position.

Resistance: 5-25 lbs.

Starting repetitions: 10.

Cadence: Slow.

Caution: Keep back and arms straight, hands on knees for support.

Principal muscles affected: Trapezius, splenius capitus, etc., of the upper back and neck.

FOR THE CHEST

*36. FORWARD RAISE ON BENCH WITH DUMBBELLS

Exercise: Refer to page 54 for the description. For men, *resistance:* 10-20 lbs. for each arm; *starting repetitions:* 10.

*37. ALTERNATE PULL-OVER WITH DUMBBELLS

Starting position: Lying position with back on floor, legs flexed at the hips so that the knees are above the chest, the lower legs extend parallel with floor from flexed knees and are crossed at the ankles. One arm is

Fig. 6—22.   Alternate pull-over with dumbbells.

extended beyond the head, palm up; the other is at the side of the body, palm down; each hand grasping a dumbbell.

Movement: (1) Bring both arms upward in an arc and down to a position reversed from the starting position. (2) Bring both arms upward in an arc and return to starting position.

Resistance: For men, 10-20 lbs.; for women, 3-5 lbs., for each arm.

Starting repetitions: For men, 10; for women, 5.

Cadence: Slow.

Caution: The knees should be raised to a position above the chest. This helps keep the lower back flat on the floor during the performance of the exercise. The arms should be kept straight throughout the exercise.

Principal muscles affected: Pectoralis major of the chest, latissimus dorsi of the back, and deltoid of the shoulder.

*38. TWO-ARMS PULL-OVER WITH BARBELL OR DUMBBELL

Exercise: Refer to pages 36 (men) and 51 (women) for the descriptions.

*39. ALTERNATE SUPINE PRESS WITH DUMBBELLS

Starting position: Lying position with back on bench, dumbbells held at shoulder height and a short distance away from the body.

Movement: Straighten the right arm at the elbow pushing the dumbbell to arm's length above the shoulder, then lower the dumbbell to starting position. As the dumbbell in the right hand is being lowered, raise the left dumbbell to arm's length above the shoulder. Keep the arms moving alternately until the prescribed number of repetitions is completed.

Resistance: For men, 10-40 lbs; for women, 3-10 lbs.; each arm.

Starting repetitions: For men, 10; for women, 5. A complete press movement by both arms constitutes one repetition.

Cadence: Moderate.

Caution: The elbows should be stretched backward at the shoulders during count 2 and the elbows should move out away from the body.

Fig. 6—23. Alternate supine press with dumbbells.

Principal muscles affected: Pectoralis major of the chest, triceps of the back of the upper arm, and deltoid of the shoulder.

*40. INCLINED-BENCH PRESS WITH DUMBBELLS

Exercise: Refer to page 47 for the description. For men, *resistance:* 10-40 lbs., each arm; *starting repetitions:* 10.

41. DECLINED-BENCH PRESS WITH DUMBBELLS

Exercise: Refer to page 91 for the description.

42. SUPINE PRESS WITH BARBELL

Exercise: Refer to page 38 for the description.

43. REGULAR PUSH-UP, USING BENCHES

Exercise: Refer to page 96 for the description.

FOR THE UPPER BACK

*44. LATERAL RAISE FROM INCLINED POSITION WITH DUMBBELLS

Starting position: Standing position, feet comfortably apart, body in-

Fig. 6—24. Lateral raise from inclined position with dumb-bells.

clined forward 90 degrees at the hips, arms extended downward toward the floor, hands grasping dumbbells, knuckles out.

Movement: (1) Bring the arms outward and upward at the shoulders as fas as possible. (2) Return to starting position.

Resistance: For men, 5-15 lbs.; for women, 3-5 lbs., each arm.

Starting repetitions: For men, 10; for women, 5.

Cadence: Slow.

Caution: The upper back should remain flat. Bend the knees if necessary. The arms should be kept straight. All movement should take place at the shoulder joint.

Principal muscles affected: Trapezius and rhomboid major and minor of the upper back and deltoid of the shoulder.

*45. SHOULDER EXTENSION FROM INCLINED POSITION WITH DUMBBELLS

Fig. 6—25. Shoulder extension from inclined position with dumbbells.

Starting position: Standing position, feet comfortably apart, body inclined forward 90 degrees at the hips, arms extended downward towards the floor, hands grasping dumbbells, knuckles out.

Movement: (1) Bring the arms backward and upward at the shoulders as far as possible. (2) Return to starting position.

Resistance: For men, 5-15 lbs.; for women, 3-5 lbs., each arm.

Starting repetitions: For men, 10; for women, 5.

Cadence: Slow.

Caution: The upper back should remain flat. Bend the knees if necessary. The arms should be kept straight. All movement should take place at the shoulder joint.

Principal muscles affected: Trapezius and teres major of the upper back, latissimus dorsi of the back, and deltoid of the shoulder.

46. ONE-ARM ROWING MOTION WITH DUMBBELL

Starting position: Inclined position, feet comfortably apart, body bent forward approximately 90 degrees at the hips, one arm resting on end of

Fig. 6—26. One-arm rowing motion with dumbbell.

bench for support, other arm extended downward, hand grasping dumbbell, knuckles front.

Movement: (1) Bend the arm, bringing the elbow out and up and the dumbbell to the shoulder. (2) Return to starting position.

Resistance: 10-40 lbs.

Starting repetitions: 5 for each arm.

Cadence: Moderate.

Caution: The back should be flat, not rounded. The elbow should be extended out to the side at shoulder level with the dumbbell coming to the chest and not back along the side of the body bringing the weight to the abdomen. The arm should be fully extended at the completion of movement 2.

Principal muscles affected: Trapezius and rhomboid major and minor of the upper back, deltoid of the shoulder, and biceps and brachialis of the front of the upper arm.

47. ROWING MOTION WITH BARBELL

Exercise: Refer to page 29 for the description.

48. ROWING MOTION WITH LEVERAGE BAR

Starting position: Standing position with the body inclined forward 90 degrees at the hips, the knees slightly bent, feet comfortably apart and

Fig. 6—27. Rowing motion with leverage bar.

astride bar which is loaded at the end nearest the shoulders only, the back flat with abdominal muscles tensed, and the arms extended downward with the hands grasping the bar with the reverse grip just beyond barbell plates.

Movement: (1) Pull the weighted end of the bar to the chest. (2) Return to starting position.

Resistance: 40-75 lbs.

Starting repetitions: 5.

Cadence: Moderate.

Caution: The back should be flat, not rounded, with the abdominal muscles tense, and should not be moved upward and downward during the performance of the exercise. The elbows should be extended to the sides at shoulder level. The arms should be fully extended at the completion of movement 2.

Principal muscles affected: Trapezius and rhomboid major and minor of the upper back, deltoid of the shoulder, and biceps and brachialis of the front of the upper arm.

*49. UPRIGHT ROWING MOTION WITH BARBELL

Starting position: Erect standing position, feet comfortably apart, arms extended downward in front of body, hands close together and grasping bar with the over-grip.

Movement: (1) Bend the elbows, extending them outward to the sides, hands bringing the bar to the height of the chest. (2) Return to starting position.

Resistance: For men, 40-75 lbs.; for women, 5-15 lbs.

Starting repetitions: 5.

Cadence: Moderate.

Fig. 6—28. Upright rowing motion with barbell.

Caution: Maintain the upright posture throughout the movement. All the movement should be at the elbows and shoulders. Do not incline the body forward and then sharply back, to aid the movement.

Principal muscles affected: Trapezius, teres minor, infraspinatus, serratus anterior of the upper back, deltoid of the shoulder, and biceps and brachialis of the front of the upper arm.

50. SITTING ROWING MOTION, USING LAT MACHINE

Starting position: Sitting position facing lat machine with knees slightly bent, feet fairly close together and supported by board or partner, arms extended forward, hands grasping bar at little more than shoulder-width apart with the over-grip.

Movement: (1) Flex the arms and extend the elbows to the sides of the body at shoulder level, bringing the bar to the chest. (2) Return to starting position.

Resistance: 40-75 lbs.

Starting repetitions: 5.

Cadence: Moderate.

Caution: The back should be flat, not rounded, and should not be moved forward and backward during performance of the exercise. The elbows should be extended to the sides with the bar coming to the chest, and not back along the sides bringing the bar to the waist. The arms should be completely extended at the completion of movement count 2.

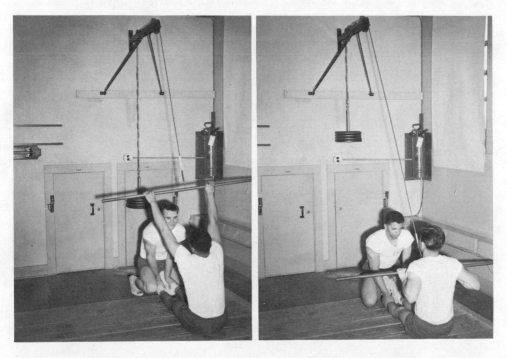

Fig. 6–29. Sitting rowing motion, using lat machine.

Principal muscles affected: Trapezius and rhomboid major and minor of the upper back, deltoid of the shoulder, and biceps and brachialis of the front of the upper arm.

51. ROWING PULL TO WAIST WITH BARBELL

Fig. 6—30. Rowing pull to waist with barbell.

Starting position: Standing position with the body inclined forward 90 degrees at the hips, the knees slightly bent, feet comfortably apart, the back flat with the abdominal muscles tensed, and the arms extended downward with the hands grasping the bar, which is on the floor, with the over-grip about shoulder-width apart.

Movement: (1) Flex the arms, bringing the elbows up close to the sides of the body and the bar to the waist. (2) Return to starting position.

Resistance: 40-75 lbs.

Starting repetitions: 5.

Cadence: Moderate.

Caution: The back should be flat, not rounded, with the abdominal muscles tensed and should not be moved upward and downward during the performance of the exercise. The arms should be fully extended at the completion of movement count 2.

Principal muscles affected: Latissimus dorsi of the back, trapezius and rhomboid major and minor of the upper back, deltoid of the shoulder, and biceps and brachialis of the front of the upper arm.

*52. ALTERNATE PULL-OVER WITH DUMBBELLS

Exercise: Refer to page 101 for the description.

*53. SINGLE-ARM SIDE PULL-OVER WITH DUMBBELL

Exercise: Refer to page 44 for the description. For men, *resistance:* 10-20 lbs.

*54. TWO-ARMS PULL-OVER WITH BARBELL OR DUMBBELL

Exercise: Refer to page 36 (men) and page 51 (women) for the description.

55. TWO-ARMS CHIN, USING CHINNING BAR

Exercise: Refer to page 86 for the description.

56. PULL-DOWN TO CHEST, USING LAT MACHINE

Exercise: Refer to page 87 for the description.

57. PULL-UP TO BACK OF NECK, USING CHINNING BAR

Exercise: Refer to page 88 for the description.

*58. PULL-DOWN TO BACK OF NECK, USING LAT MACHINE

Exercise: Refer to page 43 for the description. For men, *resistance:* 50-100 lbs.

59. SHOULDER DIPS, USING PARALLEL OR DIP BARS

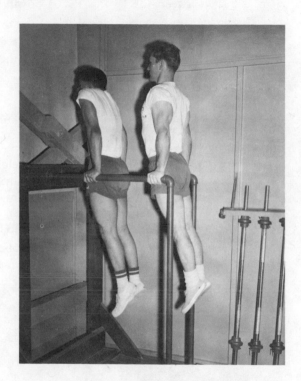

Fig. 6–31. Shoulder dips, using dip bars.

Starting position: Erect arm support position on the bars, arms straight, legs together and feet suspended above the floor.

Movement: (1) Keeping the arms straight, lower the body as far as possible bringing the shoulders close to the ears. (2) Raise the head and shoulders as far as possible.

Resistance: 20-60 lbs. Barbell plates or dumbbells attached to the front of the body by means of a belt around the waist.

Starting repetitions: 10.

Cadence: Moderate.

Caution: Keep the arms straight. This is a back, not an arm, exercise.

Principal muscles affected: Latissimus dorsi of the back, trapezius, infraspinatus, teres major and minor of the upper back, and pectoralis major and minor of the front of the chest.

FOR THE LOWER BACK

*60. ONE-ARM SWING WITH DUMBBELL

Starting position: Standing position with feet apart, knees and hips bent inclining the body forward approximately parallel with the floor. One hand is placed on the corresponding knee, the other is extended downward, hand grasping dumbbell between the legs and just off the floor.

Movement: (1) Swing the dumbbell forward and upward in an arc as far as possible straightening the body. (2) Swing the dumbbell down and back between the legs as far as possible.

Resistance: For men, 15-40 lbs.; for women, 5-10 lbs.

Starting repetitions: 10; five with the dumbbell held in the right hand, and five with the dumbbell held in the left hand.

Cadence: Moderate.

Caution: Use hand on knee for assistance. Keep arm straight throughout movement. Lean back as the weight is swung forward and forward when the weight is swung back.

Principal muscles affected: The spinal erector group (iliocostalis lumborum, longissimus dorsi, spinalis dorsi) of the lower back, gluteus maximus of the hip, quadriceps femoris (rectus femoris, vastus lateralis, vastus intermedius, vastus medialis) of the front of the thigh, the hamstrings (biceps femoris, semitendinosus, semimembranosus) of the back of the upper leg, and deltoid of the shoulder.

Variation: For men only. Toss dumbbell from one hand to the other in front of the body on the upward swing.

Fig. 6—32. One-arm swing with dumbbell.

*61. STIFF-LEGGED DEAD LIFT WITH BARBELL

Exercise: Refer to page 36 for the description. For women, *resistance:* 15-30 lbs.

*62. STIFF-LEGGED BEND-OVER WITH BARBELL

Exercise: Refer to page 50 for the description. For men, *resistance:* 30-75 lbs.

63. DEAD LIFT WITH BARBELL

Fig. 6—33. Dead lift with barbell.

Starting position: Standing position, feet comfortably apart and on line, back straight, body bent forward at hips, knees bent, hands grasping bar immediately in front of the body and resting on the floor with the over-grip, arms straight. Use reverse grip with heavy weight.

Movement: (1) Come to erect standing position. (2) Return to starting position.

Resistance: 50-150 lbs.

Starting repetitions: 10; change hand positions after five repetitions when reverse grip is used.

Caution: Keep the arms and back straight. Come to a completely erect position during each repetition.

Principal muscles affected: The spinal erector group (iliocostalis lumborum, longissimus dorsi, spinalis dorsi) of the lower back, gluteus maximus of the hip, quadriceps femoris (rectus femoris, vastus lateralis, vastus intermedius, vastus medialis) of the front of the thigh, and the hamstrings (biceps femoris, semitendinosus, semimembranosus) of the back of the upper leg.

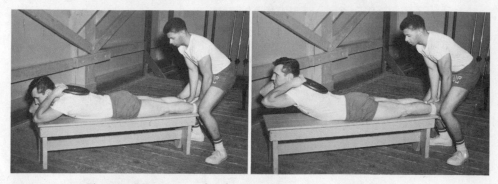

Fig. 6—34. Prone back extension with barbell plate.

*64. PRONE BACK EXTENSION WITH BARBELL PLATE

Starting position: Lying position on floor or bench, face down, legs together and straight and either fastened beneath object or held by partner, arms flexed, hands grasping barbell plate at shoulder blades.

Movement: (1) Extend the back, lifting the shoulders up off the floor or bench as far as possible. (2) Return to starting position.

Resistance: For men, 0-25 lbs.; for women, 0-5 lbs.

Starting repetitions: 10.

Cadence: Slow.

Caution: Have feet anchored securely. Extend back as far as possible.

Principal muscles affected: The spinal erector group (iliocostalis lumborum, longissimus dorsi, spinalis dorsi) of the lower back, and the gluteus maximus of the hip.

*65. ALTERNATE PRONE LEG EXTENSION WITH METAL SHOES

Starting position: Lying position on bench, face down hands grasping bench edges, feet slightly apart and extended beyond edge of bench.

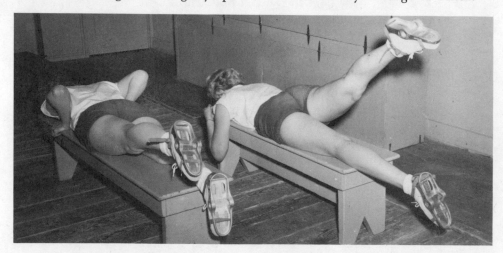

Fig. 6—35. Alternate prone leg extension with metal shoe.

Movement: Extend the right leg at the hip raising it up from the bench as far as possible, then return it to the bench. As the right leg is being lowered, raise the left leg as far as possible. Keep the legs moving alternately at the hip joints for the prescribed number of repetitions.

Resistance: 0-5 lbs. each leg.

Starting repetitions: 10. A complete extension movement by both legs constitutes one repetition.

Cadence: Moderate.

Caution: Raise leg as high as possible. Do not bend the knee.

Principal muscles affected: The spinal erector group (iliocostalis lumborum, longissimus dorsi, spinalis dorsi) of the lower back, and the gluteus maximus of the hip.

Variation: Raise both legs at the same time.

FOR THE ABDOMEN

*66. CURL-UP WITH DUMBBELL

Starting position: Lying position with back on floor, legs bent at the knees and hips so that the feet are resting on the floor close to the seat and held down by a partner or object. A dumbbell is held on the chest by grasping the outside of the globe ends with the hands.

Fig. 6—36. Curl-up with dumbbell.

Movement: (1) Tense the abdominal muscles bringing the sternum as close to the pubic bone as possible, permitting no movement at the hip joint. (2) Return to starting position.

Resistance: For men, 0-35 lbs.; for women, 0-5 lbs.

Starting repetitions: 10.

Cadence: Slow.

Caution: No hip movement is involved.

Principal muscles affected: Rectus abdominus of the abdomen.

*67. SIT-UP WITH DUMBBELL

Exercise: Refer to page 37 (men) and page 48 (women) for the description.

*68. LEG PUSH-AWAYS WITH METAL SHOES

Exercise: Refer to page 52 for the description.

*69. SIDE BEND WITH DUMBBELL

Exercise: Refer to page 33 (men) or 49 (women) for the description.

70. SIDE BEND WITH BARBELL

Fig. 6—37. Side bend with barbell.

Starting position: Erect standing position with feet apart, the barbell placed behind the neck and resting on the shoulders, hands grasping the bar out near the inside collars with the over-grip.

Movement: Bend to one side of the body as far as possible. (1) Bend to the opposite side as far as possible. (2) Return to the position specified for the start of count 1.

Resistance: 30-60 lbs.

Starting repetitions: 10.

Cadence: Moderate.

Caution: Watch the balance. The knees should be kept locked with the legs straight, the hips locked, and all movements performed at the waist. The bending should be directly sideward and not slightly forward.

Principal muscles affected: External and internal oblique muscles at the sides of the waist.

71. TWISTING SIDE BEND WITH DUMBBELL

Starting position: Erect standing position with feet apart, one forearm placed in the small of the back, the other arm extended overhead, hand grasping dumbbell.

Fig. 6—38. Twisting side bend with dumbbell.

Movement: (1) Bend sideward and forward at the hips, waist, and knee opposite the weight hand, touching the shoulder of the same side to that knee. (2) Return to starting position.

Resistance: 10-25 lbs.

Starting repetitions: 20; ten with the dumbbell held in the right hand, and ten with the dumbbell held in the left hand.

Cadence: Slow.

Caution: Watch the balance; keeping the eyes on the dumbbell held overhead will help this. The leg on the weight side of the body should remain straight. Assuming the bent-over position may prove difficult for some. Assuming the squat position of a football halfback with the elbows resting on the thighs, then moving one hand overhead and the opposite shoulder to the knee will aid the person get the "feel" of the position. From this position, the subject should straighten the leg on the weight side of the body and then move to an erect position.

Principal muscles affected: External and internal oblique muscles of the sides of the waist, the gluteus maximus of the hip, and the spinal erector group (iliocostalis lumborum, longissimus dorsi, spinalis dorsi) of the lower back.

FOR THE LEG AND HIP

*72. HALF-SQUAT WITH BARBELL

Exercise: Refer to pages 34 (men) and 45 (women) for the description.

73. FRONT HALF-SQUAT WITH BARBELL

Starting position: Erect standing position with feet comfortably apart,

Fig. 6—39. Front half-squat with barbell.

the bar held at the chest with the hands about shoulder-width apart with the over-grip, elbows bent and extended forward of bar.

Movement: (1) Perform a half-squat or knee bend so that the angle at the knee joint approaches a right angle. (2) Return to starting position.

Resistance: 40-75 lbs.

Starting repetitions: 10.

Cadence: Moderate.

Caution: The back should remain straight during the performance of the exercise. The elbows should be thrust well forward beneath the bar to maintain the weight at the chest. If balance is a problem due to limited ankle flexibility, place a barbell plate or piece of wood under the heels. The knees should not be bent to less than a right angle in the performance of this exercise.

Principal muscles affected: Quadriceps femoris (rectus femoris, vastus lateralis, vastus intermedius, vastus medialis) of the front of the upper leg or thigh, hamstrings (biceps femoris, semitendinosus, semimembranosus) of the back of the upper leg, and gluteus maximus of the hip.

74. STRADDLE LIFT WITH BARBELL

Exercise: Refer to page 31 for the description.

75. HACK LIFT WITH BARBELL

Starting position: Erect standing position with heels close together on raised block of wood, arms extended downward, hands close together grasping the bar behind the hips with the over-grip.

Movement: (1) Perform a half-squat or knee bend so that the angle at the knee joint approaches a right angle. (2) Return to starting position.

Fig. 6—40. Hack lift with barbell.

Resistance: 40-75 lbs.

Starting repetitions: 10.

Cadence: Moderate.

Caution: Perform a half-squat only. The back should remain straight and upright during performance of the exercise.

Principal muscles affected: Quadriceps femoris (rectus femoris, vastus lateralis, vastus intermedius, vastus medialis) of the front of the upper leg or thigh, hamstrings (biceps femoris, semitendinosus, semimembranosus) of the back of the upper leg, and gluteus maximus of the hip.

76. LEG PRESS WITH BARBELL

Starting position: Lying position on back, arms at sides, legs extended upward at the hips, feet supporting a barbell.

Movement: (1) Bend the knees and hips, lowering the bar to a position above the chest. (2) Extend the legs and return to starting position.

Resistance: 40-150 lbs.

Starting repetitions: 10.

Cadence: Slow.

Caution: This exercise should not be performed alone. A spotter should be at each end of the bar to place the weight on the feet and to take the weight should it slip. Always keep the toes raised higher than the heels to prevent the weight sliding off toward the face. Keep the lower legs perpendicular to the floor as the knees and hips are flexed and the eyes on the weight, for balance.

Principal muscles affected: Quadriceps femoris (rectus femoris, vastus lateralis, vastus intermedius, vastus medialis) of the front of the upper

Fig. 6—41.   Leg press with barbell.

leg, hamstrings (biceps femoris, semitendinosus, semimembranosus) of the back of the upper leg, and gluteus maximus of the hip.

Substitution: The use of a leg press machine will eliminate much of the problem and danger of this exercise.

*77. SINGLE-LEG EXTENSION WITH METAL SHOE

Exercise: Refer to page 52 for the description. For men, *resistance:* 5-25 lbs.

*78. BICYCLE WITH METAL SHOES

Starting position: Lying position with back on floor and hips supported in the air by the hands, elbows on the floor. The legs are extended directly above the hips with metal shoes attached to the feet.

Fig. 6—42.   Bicycle with metal shoes.

Movement: Bend the knees and the hips, moving each leg alternately, so that the movement of the feet will describe a circle similar to that described by the feet of a person pedaling a bicycle.

Resistance: For men, 5-25 lbs.; for women, 2½-5 lbs., each leg.

Starting repetitions: 10. The describing of a complete circle by both feet constitutes one repetition.

Cadence: Moderate.

Caution: The exerciser should make certain of his or her balance before starting the bicycle movement and start slowly or he might be pulled off balance by the weight of the shoes.

Principal muscles affected: Quadriceps femoris (rectus femoris, vastus lateralis, vastus intermedius, vastus medialis) of the front of the upper leg, hamstrings (biceps femoris, semitendinosus, semimembranosus) of the back of the upper leg, and gluteus maximus of the hip.

*79. ALTERNATE PRONE LEG EXTENSION WITH METAL SHOES

Exercise: Refer to page 112 for the description.

*80. SINGLE-LEG BACK EXTENSION WITH METAL SHOE

Exercise: Refer to page 53 for the description.

*81. STRAIGHT-LEGGED BICYCLE WITH METAL SHOES

Exercise: Refer to page 54 for the description.

*82. STIFF-LEGGED DEAD LIFT WITH BARBELL

Exercise: Refer to page 36 for the description. For women, *resistance:* 15-30 lbs.

*83. STIFF-LEGGED BEND-OVER WITH BARBELL OR DUMBBELL

Exercise: Refer to page 50 for the description. For men, *resistance:* 30-75 lbs.

*84. ALTERNATE PRONE LEG CURL WITH METAL SHOES

Starting position: Lying position, face down on bench, arms at sides grasping edges of bench, feet extended beyond bench end. Metal shoes attached to both feet.

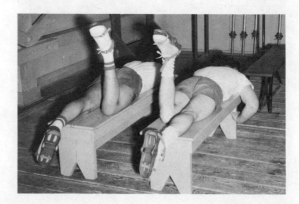

Fig. 6—43. Alternate prone leg curl with metal shoes.

Movement: Bend the right leg at the knee, bringing the metal shoe to a position close to the right hip; then extend the leg at the knee joint, returning it to the starting position. As the right leg is being returned to the starting position, bend the left leg at the knee, bringing the metal shoe to a position close to the left hip. Keep the legs moving alternately at the knees until the prescribed number of repetitions is completed.

Resistance: For men, 5-25 lbs.; for women, 2½-5 lbs., each leg.

Starting repetitions: 10. A complete leg curl movement by both legs constitutes one repetition.

Cadence: Slow.

Caution: The feet should extend beyond the end of the bench but the lower leg should not. Move the leg slowly towards full extension so as not to place stress on the knee joint.

Principal muscles affected: Hamstrings (biceps femoris, semitendinosus, semimembranosus) of the back of the upper leg, and gastrocnemius of the back of the lower leg.

*85. SINGLE-LEG CURL WITH METAL SHOE

Starting position: Erect standing position near a wall or fixed object with hands resting against it for support. Metal shoes attached to both feet.

Movement: (1) Bend one leg at the knee, bringing the metal shoe to a position near the hip. (2) Return to starting position.

Resistance: For men, 5-25 lbs.; for women, 2½-5 lbs.

Fig. 6—44. Single-leg curl with metal shoe.

Starting repetitions: 10, each leg.

Cadence: Slow.

Caution: All the movement should take place at the knee joint. Do not move the knee forward during the performance of the exercise.

Principal muscles affected: Hamstrings (biceps femoris, semitendinosus, semimembranosus) of the back of the upper leg, and gastrocnemius of the back of the lower leg.

*86. SIDE-LYING LEG SCISSORS WITH METAL SHOE

Exercise: Refer to page 53 for the description.

*87. SIDE-LYING LEG ABDUCTION WITH METAL SHOE

Fig. 6—45. Side lying leg abduction with metal shoe.

Starting position: Lying position with side of body on floor, under arm extended beyond head on floor and supporting head, upper arm extended in front of the body, hand on the floor for balance, legs straight, one resting above the other, metal shoe attached to upper foot.

Movement: (1) Raise the top-resting leg upward as far as possible. (2) Return to starting position.

Resistance: 2½-5 lbs.

Starting repetitions: 10, each leg. The right side of the body will recline on the floor when the left leg is performing the movement, and vice versa.

Cadence: Slow.

Caution: The hips should remain at right angles with the floor and not tilted backward as the leg is raised upward as far as possible.

Principal muscles affected: Abductor (tensor fascia latae, gluteus medius, gluteus minimus) muscles of the hip.

Fig. 6—46. Single-leg abduction with metal shoe.

*88. SINGLE-LEG ABDUCTION WITH METAL SHOE

Starting position: Erect standing position near a wall or fixed object with one hand resting against it for support, the other hand placed on the hip. Metal shoes attached to both feet.

Movement: (1) Raise the leg furthest from the wall sideways as far as possible. (2) Return to starting position.

Resistance: 2½-5 lbs.

Starting repetitions: 10 each leg.

Cadence: Slow.

Caution: Keep the body erect throughout the movement. Do not turn the body toward the direction in which the movement is taking place.

Principal muscles affected: Abductor (tensor fascia latae, gluteus medius, gluteus minimus) muscles of the hip.

*89. SUPINE LEG ADDUCTION WITH METAL SHOES

Starting position: Lying position with back on floor, arms on floor at sides for support, legs extended directly above the hips with metal shoes attached to the feet.

Movement: (1) Spread the legs sideward as far as possible. (2) Return to starting position.

Resistance: 2½-5 lbs., each leg.

Starting repetitions: 10.

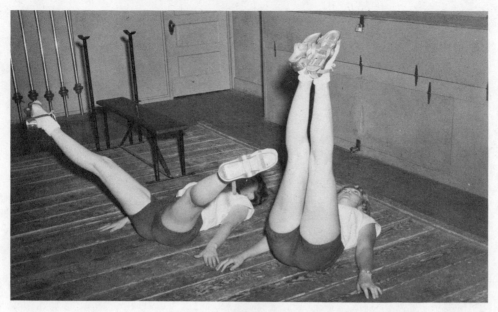

Fig. 6—47. Supine leg adduction with metal shoes.

Cadence: Slow.

Caution: Use the arms for balance. Do not spread the legs too rapidly.

Principal muscles affected: Adductor (gracilis, pectineus, adductor longus, adductor brevis, adductor magnus) muscles of the upper leg.

90. RISE ON ONE FOOT WITH DUMBBELL

Fig. 6—48. Rise on one foot with dumbbell.

Starting position: Erect standing position near a wall or fixed object with one hand resting against it for support, the other arm extended downward at the side, hand grasping dumbbell. The foot on the side opposite the dumbbell hand is held off the floor.

Movement: (1) Rise up on the ball and toes of the one foot. (2) Return to starting position.

Resistance: 15-50 lbs.

Starting repetitions: 10 each foot.

Cadence: Slow.

Caution: Keep the body erect, do not bend forward at the hip during the movement. Rise upward as far as possible during each repetition.

Principal muscles affected: Calf muscles (gastrocnemius and soleus) of the back of the lower leg.

*91. RISE ON TOES WITH BARBELL OR DUMBBELL

Exercise: Refer to page 32 (men) and page 45 (women) for the description.

92. DONKEY HEEL RAISES WITH PARTNER

Fig. 6—49.   Donkey heel raises with partner.

Starting position: Standing position, feet comfortably apart, body inclined forward 90 degrees at the hips, hands grasping fixed object for support, partner sitting astride the back at the hips in horse and rider position.

Movement: (1) Rise up on the balls of feet and toes. (2) Return to starting position.

Resistance: Weight of partner.

Starting repetitions: 20; ten with the toes pointed in, and 10 with the toes pointed out.

Cadence: Slow.

Caution: The knees should remain locked throughout the performance of the exercise. A solid object must be grasped for support. Rise upward as far as possible and see that the feet have a definite inward or outward slant, depending on the phase of the exercise.

Principal muscles affected: Calf (gastrocnemius and soleus) muscles of the back of the lower leg.

93. RISE ON HEELS WITH BARBELL

Starting position: Erect standing position with feet comfortably apart and heels placed on raised board or piece of wood, the bar placed behind the neck and resting on the shoulders, hands grasping the bar out near the inside collars with the over-grip.

Movement: (1) Rise up on the heels. (2) Return to starting position.

Resistance: 40-75 lbs.

Starting repetitions: 10.

Cadence: Slow.

Caution: The back should remain erect and the knees locked throughout performance of the exercise.

Principal muscles affected: Muscles (tibialis anterior, extensor digitorum longus, peroneus tertius) of the front of the lower leg.

SPECIAL EXERCISE PROGRAMS
FOR FUNDAMENTAL PHYSICAL SKILLS

Certain fundamental movements or basic skills are utilized in the performance of the sports and athletic events that are so popular among boys and girls and men and women, particularly of secondary school and college age. These basic physical skills include climbing, jumping, lifting, running, throwing, vaulting, etc.; some of which are involved in all the various sports and athletic events. Performance in these fundamental skills is of interest to the participant and coach alike; for the better such performance, other things being equal, the better the performance in the sport or event utilizing these skills or specific variations of them.

The following lists give recommended exercise programs for the specific muscle groups that are of particular importance for several fundamental physical skills. The number following the exercise refers to its place in the sequence of exercise descriptions in this chapter.

CLIMBING

1. Two-arms curl with barbell (1)
2. One-arm triceps extension with dumbbell (21)
3. Wrist curl with barbell (27)
4. Pull-down to chest, using lat machine (7)
5. One-arm concentration curl with dumbbell (5)
6. Half-squat with barbell (72)
7. Two-arms press with barbell (10)
8. Two-arms pullover with barbell (38)

9. Wrist roll, using wrist roll machine or stick and rope (26)
10. Front and lateral raise with dumbbells (31)
11. Stiff-legged dead lift with barbell (61)
12. Rowing pull to waist with barbell (51)
13. Sit-up with dumbbell (67)
14. Hack lift with barbell (75)
15. Alternate grasping with barbell plate (30)

JUMPING AND RUNNING

1. Two-arms curl with barbell (1)
2. Two-arms press with barbell (10)
3. Hack lift with barbell (75)
4. Shoulder shrug with barbell (33)
5. Rowing motion with barbell (47)
6. Half-squat with barbell (72)
7. Front and lateral raise with dumbbells (31)
8. Rise on toes with barbell (91)
9. Sit-up with dumbbell (67)
10. Stiff-legged dead lift with barbell (61)
11. Single-leg back extension with metal shoe (80)
12. Alternate prone leg curl with metal shoes (84)
13. Straight-legged bicycle with metal shoes (81)
14. Supine leg adduction with metal shoes (89)
15. Two-arms pullover with barbell (38)

THROWING

1. Two-arms curl with barbell (1)
2. Press behind neck with barbell (11)
3. Pull-down to back of neck, using lat machine (9)
4. Shoulder shrug with barbell (33)
5. Declined bench press with dumbbells (41)
6. Half-squat with barbell (72)
7. One-arm concentration curl with dumbbell (5)
8. Side bend with dumbbell (69)
9. Stiff-legged dead lift with barbell (61)
10. Two-arms pullover with barbell (38)
11. Wrist curl with barbell (27)
12. Supine press with barbell (16)
13. Twisting side bend with dumbbell (71)
14. Rise on toes with barbell (91)
15. Sit-up with dumbbell (67)
16. Lateral wrist curl with bar and weight (29)

VAULTING

1. Two-arms curl with barbell (1)
2. Two-arms press with barbell (10)

3. Pull-down to chest using lat machine (7)
4. Straddle lift with barbell (74)
5. Rise on toes with barbell (91)
6. One-arm concentration curl with dumbbell (5)
7. Wrist roll, using wrist-roll machine or stick and rope (26)
8. Triceps extension with barbell (17)
9. Half-squat with barbell (72)
10. Supine press with barbell (16)
11. Stiff-legged dead lift with barbell (61)
12. Wrist curl with barbell (27)
13. Sit-up with dumbbell (67)
14. Two-arms pullover with barbell (38)
15. Side bend with dumbbell (69)

LIFTING

The methods of performing the three Olympic lifts, which are the basis for judging competition in weight-lifting contests, are presented in Chapter 7. Programs for the development of the strength necessary to enter this type of competition have already been presented. There are, however, several exercises that aid in developing form, speed, and strength in performing the two quick lifts—the snatch and the clean and jerk. These will be presented here. They should be practiced by those desiring to develop their skill and certainly before any heavy poundage is attempted.

TWO-HANDS DEAD HANG REPETITION SNATCH

Starting position: Erect standing position, feet comfortably apart, arms extended downward at sides of body, hands grasping bar held in front of hips at somewhat more than shoulder-width apart with the over-grip.

Movement: (1) Bend the hips and the knees, lowering the bar until it nearly touches the floor. (2) Lift the bar straight upward as far as possible, rising upon the balls of the feet. (3) Drop the body under the weight by either (a) moving one foot to the front and one to the rear or (b) squatting beneath the weight, and catch it at arm's length overhead. (4) Rise to a standing position with the weight held overhead.

Resistance: 75-100 lbs., with increases as one becomes more proficient.

Starting repetitions: 5. The four parts described under movement are performed in succession and constitute one repetition.

Cadence: Moderate.

Caution: Practice dropping as low beneath the weight as possible in catching it. Start with a sufficiently light weight so that balance is not lost.

TWO-HANDS DEAD HANG REPETITION CLEAN

Exercise: Performed in the same manner as the two-hands dead hang snatch, except that the weight is caught at the chest instead of at arm's length overhead.

TWO-HANDS REPETITION JERK

Starting position: Erect standing position with feet comfortably apart; the bar held at the chest with the hands about shoulder-width apart and with the over-grip, elbows bent and extended forward of the bar.

Movement: (1) Dip slightly, bending the knees and hips. (2) Extend the legs and arms forcibly pushing the bar upward as far as possible. (3) Drop the body under the weight by splitting one leg forward and the other back, catching the bar at arm's length overhead. (4) Rise to a standing position with the weight held overhead.

Resistance: 100-150 lbs., increasing the resistance as one becomes more proficient.

Starting repetitions: 5. The four parts described under movement are performed in succession and constitute one repetition.

Cadence: Moderate.

Caution: Practice dropping as low beneath the weight as possible in catching it. Plant the feet solidly at the completion of the split. Start with a weight sufficiently light so that balance is not lost.

If, in practicing the three lifts described above, or any other heavy lift, the weight is not caught, but missed, and the performer is off balance, then step out of the way and let it come down. Do not attempt to catch a weight when out of position or off balance.

USE OF PROGRESSIVE WEIGHT TRAINING EXERCISES IN THE CORRECTIVE PROGRAM

The preventive aspect of postural abnormalities has been stressed here in the descriptions of the methods of performing the various exercises—hence the admonition to adhere closely to the method of performance described.

In the regular physical education program, the teacher will come into contact with many who are sub-par physically; i.e., those lacking in physical strength and size. To prescribe a weight training program for them is certainly fitting, provided the youngster has no physical defects. The medical record and, if indicated, the youngster's physician should be consulted before commencing any program of this type.

Knee injuries were one of the first types that drew medical attention to the use of weights. Certain postural deviations, also, are particularly suited for weight exercises. Several exercises for knee cases and postural deviations are presented below. However, when performing any work of a corrective nature, always work through a physician and have his approval for the activity. He is the one licensed to prescribe treatment.

FOR STRENGTHENING QUADRICEPS AND TIGHTENING KNEE JOINT FOLLOWING INJURY

1. SINGLE LEG EXTENSION, WITH METAL SHOE

Exercise: Refer to page 60 for the description. De Lorme [2] recommends the use of three sets of ten repetitions each in the practice of this exercise. The first set is performed with a resistance that is one-half the maximum the subject can lift for ten repetitions. The second set is performed with three-fourths the maximum amount, and the third with the maximum amount. Do not permit the subjects' foot to hang from the bench between exercise sets, but have him rest it on the bench or some object to relieve the downward pull of the weight.

2. KNEE TURNS

Starting position: Erect standing position, feet comfortably apart.
Movement: (1) Without moving the feet or bending the knees, turn the legs and knees inward. (2) Without moving the feet or bending the knees, turn the legs and knees outward. *Repetitions:* Three sets of ten each.

TO ASSIST THE CORRECTION OF KYPHOSIS (ABNORMAL UPPER BACK CURVATURE, ROUND SHOULDERS)

TWO-ARMS PULL-OVER WITH BARBELL OR DUMBBELL

Exercise: Refer to page 51 for the description. A light weight is used in performing this exercise, and a rolled towel is placed along the spine between the shoulder blades.

TO ASSIST THE CORRECTION OF LORDOSIS (ABNORMAL LOWER BACK CURVATURE, SWAY BACK)

LEG PUSH-AWAYS

Exercise: Refer to page 52 for the description. Straighten the legs as far as possible each time without creating an arch in the lower back. Attempt to increase the degree of leg straightness until the legs can be nearly straightened out on the floor without creating an arch in the lower back.

TO ASSIST THE CORRECTION OF SCOLIOSIS (LATERAL CURVATURE OF THE SPINE)

SINGLE-ARM SIDE PULL-OVER WITH DUMBBELL

Exercise: Refer to page 44 for the description. The convex or protruding side should be toward the bench or floor. A rolled towel is placed beneath this area. The subject uses the weight to stretch the spine when arm is extended beyond head.

2 T. L. De Lorme and A. L. Watkins, "Technics of Progressive Resistance Exercise," *Archives of Physical Medicine*, Vol. 29 (1948), p. 263, as reported in Sidney Licht (ed.), Therapeutic Exercise (New Haven: Elizabeth Licht, Publisher, 1958), p. 291.

7

Weight Lifting

Weight lifting, as a spectator sport, does not enjoy the popularity afforded the American seasonal team sports of football, basketball, and baseball. It is a different type of activity—one that calls for an aesthetic type of appreciation of the feat accomplished, much the same as that needed to enjoy a fine gymnastic demonstration or dance performance. Such appreciation is usually gained only from first-hand experience in the handling of weights. Without this experience a person has little or no concept of what is involved in lifting a heavy weight to arm's length overhead. In the past, when manual labor was a necessity for a large segment of our population, this appreciation was more widespread than it is today; the attendance at lifting demonstrations and contests then was greater than today when the spectators are primarily the individuals, and their families, who are in some manner engaged in the activity.

The writer does not wish to imply that weight lifting, as a sport, is on the way out. This is not so. On the contrary, the sport enjoys A.A.U. sponsorship in many localities as well as at the national level. It is now reaching the colleges where weight lifting teams are sponsored and intra- and inter-school contests are being arranged. National competition at this level is already a reality. It is just that the spectator interest of nonparticipants is not great.

At a properly sponsored weight lifting meet an observer finds spectator seating much the same as it is at any other sports event. The participants are usually seated near the platform where the lifting is to take place. One regulation barbell is on the platform. Two judges and a referee are seated, usually one on each of three sides of the four-sided platform. They officiate the contest, and an affirmative vote by any two of them indicates a satisfactory performance by the lifter. In addition to these three officials, a regulation meet requires two scorers and a weigher as well. Two loaders, one at each side of the platform which is approximately thirteen feet square, load the bar to whatever weight is requested.

Competition in each of the three recognized Olympic lifts takes place separately; i.e., the contestants will compete in the press first, then the snatch, and finally the clean and jerk. Each contestant is permitted three attempts at each lift, irrespective of whether the lift is a success or a failure. The officials and lifters decide the lowest poundage that will be attempted, and the bar is loaded to that weight. The lifter who has selected this poundage is then called to the platform by the judges. He is given the signal to proceed by the referee, who also signals the completion of the lift. The lift is then rated as acceptable or not by the vote of the referee and judges. If the lifter fails the lift, he may again attempt the same weight. He may *not* attempt a lower weight. If the lifter succeeds with the weight, the second attempt must be made with a weight at least ten pounds in excess of the first; and if successful here, the third attempt must be with a weight at least five pounds in excess of the second. Each contestant calls for the weight he wishes to attempt as the bar is loaded to progressively heavier weights in the progress of the contest.

The atmosphere at a contest is one of extreme quiet—so quiet, in fact, that one can hear the proverbial pin drop. It is not uncommon to see the lifter spend a good deal of time just standing above the weight and looking at it. The effort represents the peak or near peak of his performance, and he must convince himself that he is the master of that piece of iron and can and will lift it successfully in the manner prescribed. Any undue noise may break the spell of concentration, and he will have to set himself again, mentally, before attempting the weight. He may huff and puff quite loudly during this mental set. However, once the lift is begun, the lifter holds his breath until it, or a particular phase of it in the case of a two-stage lift, is completed.

THE OLYMPIC LIFTS[1]

Competition, as mentioned previously, takes place in each of three lifts: the two-hands military press, the two-hands snatch, and the two-hands clean and jerk. The individual lifting the greatest amount of weight in terms of total pounds lifted (the sum total of the best of each of the three lifts) is adjudged the winner in his weight class. In case of a tie, the victory goes to the man lightest in body weight.

THE TWO-HANDS MILITARY PRESS.   In this lift, the bar is grasped with the over-grip and brought to the chest in one continuous movement. It is held there for a period of two seconds. The referee signals the conclusion of this time with a clap of the hands. Then, with the feet parallel and on line and with no assisting movement of the body or legs, the weight is pressed steadily to arms' length overhead where it must be held for two full seconds. The completion of the lift is signaled by a second clap of the referee's hands.

One of the most frequent causes for disqualification in this lift is back

[1] Bob Hoffman, *Weight Lifting* (York, Pa.: Strength and Health Publishing Co., 1939).

Fig. 7—1. Two-hands military press; Dick Krell, 132¼ lb. class, pressing 205 lbs.

Courtesy of Robert Hasse

bend. Some back curvature is usually permissible at the start of the lift, but it is not to be increased during the performance.

THE TWO-HANDS SNATCH.   In this lift, the bar is grasped with the over-grip and is brought from the position on the floor immediately in front of the lifter's ankles to arms' length overhead in one continuous movement. In performing this lift, the body may be lowered by splitting (i.e., moving one leg forward and the other back) or by squatting (doing a deep knee-bend).   In either case the arms must be locked straight without any press

Courtesy of Robert Hasse

Fig. 7—2.   Split snatch position; Juan Torres of Cuba, 148¾ lb. class, snatching 231½ lbs.

Fig. 7–3. Squat snatch position; Walter Imahara, 132¼ lb. class, snatching 220 lbs.

Courtesy of Robert Hasse

out with the arm muscles. From this split or squat position, the lifter must rise to an erect standing position with the weight held at arms' length overhead and maintain this erect standing position for a period of two seconds. The completion of the lift will be signaled by a clap from the referee.

In performing this lift, the lifter pulls the weight up in front of his body as high as he can, coming up on the balls of the feet. Then, before the weight has an opportunity to drop any distance, he must lower his body immediately, either by splitting or squatting, to a position where he can catch this weight overhead with outstretched arms.

The method of splitting the legs, one forward and one backward, seems to be the position of greatest balance support, and the one from which it is easiest to recover to the erect position. Most beginners will have trouble splitting the legs far enough to drop to a sufficiently low position to catch the weight with the outstretched arms. The heavier the weight, the more difficult it becomes because of the insecurity of the position. A low split with a heavy weight comes only after much practice.

The method of squatting beneath a weight has an advantage in that the body can be lowered somewhat farther than it can in the split position. However it does have several disadvantages in that balance is more difficult to maintain, and it is a difficult position from which to rise to gain the standing position. Many lifters using this style wear shoes with elevated heels to assist them with the problem of balance. Practice is certainly a requisite for success in this style of lifting as well. A wide grip of the hands is usually employed in both styles.

THE TWO-HANDS CLEAN AND JERK. As with the press, the bar is taken from the floor to the chest in one continuous movement. However, since in most instances the weight being lifted in this movement will be considerably greater than the amount that can be pressed, it requires more of an

Fig. 7—4. Split clean position; Vladimir Stogov of Russia, 123¼ lb. class, cleaning 286½ lbs.

Courtesy of Robert Hasse

effort to bring this weight to the chest, and the split or squat method is used to lower the body sufficiently to catch the weight at the chest. The elbows must be thrust beneath and considerably forward of the bar to maintain it in this position. With the weight in this position, the lifter must rise to an erect standing position. This is the first part of the lift, the clean. In performing the lift, the lifter does not have to hold the weight at the chest for any given length of time but may proceed immediately with the jerk. In the jerk, the weight is again raised from its position at the chest to arms' length overhead as is in the press. It differs from the press in that this upward movement may be assisted by the back and legs. The lifter takes a slight dip with his legs and then thrusts them upward, imparting as much power to the bar as possible with his legs, back, and arms. As the bar

Courtesy of Robert Hasse

Fig. 7—5. Squat clean position; Isaac Berger, 132¼ lb. class, cleaning 314¼ lbs.

Fig. 7—6. Split jerk position; Isaac Berger jerking 319 lbs.

Courtesy of Robert Hasse

reaches its maximum height, the lifter drops beneath the weight, splitting one leg to the front, the other to the rear, and catching the weight at arms' length overhead. From this split position, the lifter must rise to an erect standing position with the weight held at arms' length overhead and maintain this erect standing position for a period of two seconds. The completion of the lift will be signaled by a clap from the referee.

In the performance of this lift, lifters may vary in the method used in performing the clean; i.e., split or squat method. Nearly all lifters, however, employ the split method with the jerk.

WEIGHT LIFTING CONTEST SCORING. To equalize the opportunity for all participants, lifters compete within weight classes, as is done in boxing and wrestling. These classes or divisions are: 123¼ lbs., 132¼ lbs., 148¾ lbs., 165¼ lbs., 181¼ lbs., 198¼ lbs., and heavyweight. The total pounds lifted (i.e., the sum of the lifters best efforts in each of the three lifts) is his score for the meet. If the lifters best efforts are a press of 250 lbs., a snatch of 260 lbs., and a clean and jerk of 320 lbs., his total or score for the meet would be 830 lbs. If no one in his weight division lifts more, he would be the winner for that division. If another lifter in this division equals this total but is slightly heavier in bodyweight, the first individual, because he is lighter in body weight but still within the weight division, would be adjudged the winner.

Team winners in weight lifting are determined in much the same manner as are team winners in a track meet.[2] Each lifter who is a winner in his weight division is awarded a certain number of points (10) in U. S. and international competition. The person placing second in his division is also awarded a certain number of points (5—U. S., 6—international) and the person placing third (4), fourth (3), fifth (2) and sixth (1). The team whose lifters score the greatest number of total points is adjudged the winning team. Other competing teams are ranked according to total number of points won.

TABLE 9

WORLD WEIGHT LIFTING RECORDS [3]

Class	Press	Snatch	Clean and Jerk	Three-Lift Total
123¼	242½ Vinci USA	231¼ Stogov USSR	307½ Chen Tse Kai China	760 Stogov USSR
132¼	261 Korge USSR	250 Zielinski Poland	325 Berger USA	821 Berger USA
148¾	287½ Nikitin USSR	275½ Kostylev USSR	347½ Howe Liang Tan Singapore	859½ Bushuev USSR
165¼	308½ Timochenko USSR	294½ Kono USA	373½ Kurinov USSR	947 Kono USA
181¼	331½ Paterni France	310½ Plyukfelder USSR	393 Palinski Poland	1008 Plyukfelder USSR
198¼	338½ Gitetski USSR	321¼ Osypa USSR	408 Emrich USA	1029½ Vorobyov USSR
Heavy-weight	408¾ Anderson USA	337½ Vlasov USSR	434¾ Vlasov USSR	1130 Anderson USA

PHYSIQUE CONTESTS: THEIR CONDUCT AND SCORING

Contests involving competition in excellence of physique are held in conjunction with many weight lifting meets, and they, too, are on local, district, national, and international bases. The winner of such a contest is dubbed with the title "Mr. Spokane," "Mr. Pacific Northwest," "Mr. Pacific Coast," "Mr. America," "Mr. Universe," or "Mr." whatever the area the contest is supposed to represent. There are specific rules for the conduct of physique contests just as for any sports meet.

[2] This information is furnished by John Terpak of York, Pa.

[3] Charles Coster, "Present World Records on the Three Olympic Lifts," *Muscle Builder,* Vol. 10, No. 6 (July 1960), p. 19.

Fig. 7—7. Robert Felker, who won the "Mr. Pacific North-west" physique title while a student at Eastern Washing-ton College of Education.

The contestants line up on the stage before the judges so that all may be viewed. Each contestant is called out in turn and mounts a small plat-form, if used, in the center of the stage. He is given fifteen seconds to dis-play his physique from the back, front, and any other optional view he de-sires to present and then descends from the platform. Each contestant is called out three times. The poses that each contestant uses are those he has worked on previously and has selected as displaying his physique to the best advantage. He practices these poses and smoothes out his move-ment in going from one pose to the next so that the best artistic effect in terms of posing and movement is presented at the contest.

From five to seven persons serves as judges and rate the contestants on the following bases [4]:

Symmetry	0–5 points
Muscular Development	0–5 points
General Appearance	0–5 points
Athletic Ability *	0–5 points
Possible total	20 points

[4] Amateur Athletic Union, *Weightlifting, Official Rules,* 1959.

* The ability of the contestant as a performer in his athletic specialty; weight lifting, track, swimming, or whatever it may be.

The high and low scores given each athlete by a judge are eliminated and the rating is the total number of points given by the other judges. In addition to the "Mr." title award, other awards may be given for the "most muscular," "best arms," "best chest," "best abdomen," "best back," and "best legs" in the contest.

Index

NOTE: Exercises for the various muscles are listed under the main entry, Muscles, exercises for.